THE EVOLUTION OF CANADA'S FLORA

The Evolution of Canada's Flora

commemorating the founding meeting of
THE CANADIAN BOTANICAL ASSOCIATION
L'ASSOCIATION BOTANIQUE DU CANADA
held at Carleton University, Ottawa, May 1965

Edited by ROY L. TAYLOR
and R. A. LUDWIG

UNIVERSITY OF TORONTO PRESS

Copyright Canada, 1966, by
University of Toronto Press
Printed in Canada

Decorations by ILGVAR STEINS

Preface

THE PAPERS COMPRISING the chapters of this book are the contributions to the colloquium presented to the Founding Meeting of the Canadian Botanical Association held at Carleton University, Ottawa, in May of 1965. Our goal was to highlight the occasion with the presentation of a series of original technical papers on some distinctly Canadian aspect of botany by distinguished Canadian botanical scientists.

Canada's flora does not display the richness of a tropical flora nor can it boast the antiquity of an old-world flora. It is, however, unique in its newness, since it began with the last glaciation and is still expanding northward as glaciers recede and climate moderates. We are, in short, witnessing "evolution on the march." What then could be more distinctly Canadian and better mark the historic occasion of the founding than our theme and title, *The Evolution of Canada's Flora*?

One cannot think of the status of botany in Canada without a feeling of admiration for a few devoted pioneer students who laid the foundations of our science as it exists today. To one of these, Frère Marie-Victorin, we respectfully dedicate this volume.

We would like to express our appreciation to both the Royal Society of Canada and the National Research Council of Canada for the continued interest and financial assistance which enabled the Canadian Botanical Association to present and publish this colloquium.

R. A. LUDWIG, *President*
R. L. TAYLOR, *Secretary*
Canadian Botanical Association

Contents

THE EVOLUTION OF CANADA'S FLORA

MARCEL RAYMOND

Personal Recollections of Frère Marie-Victorin

IT IS AN HONOUR AND A PRIVILEGE to address such an eclectic group in a circumstance such as that of the founding of a society of Canadian botanists. This founding meeting is particularly apropos because the plant sciences are playing an increasing role in the expanding Canadian economy, and there are increasing demands for well-qualified botanists to participate in the development of our country's two top industries, forestry and agriculture.

It is also a personal pleasure for me to recall to all of you the image of a man who was ahead of his time, a true Canadian, a well-known scientist, a brilliant educator—a man who has left his mark in many fields. He would have loved a gathering such as the present one, because all his active life, he gave so much of his time and energy to various societies, large and well known as well as small and obscure ones, much as he saw that he could promote an interest in and a better knowledge of this very important green world that surrounds us. I cannot forget that it was at his instigation and with his help that I delivered my first botanical lecture quite a while ago.

I met frère Marie-Victorin in 1935 in appropriate surroundings. I was travelling with a cousin of mine towards Farnham, in southern Quebec, when we saw an animated group of people moving about in a bog. Outside of botanists, only blueberry-pickers dare wander through bogs! These people were obviously not berry-pickers but, undoubtedly botanists. I walked towards the group and was met by a tall man with a pleasant face and a wide forehead, wearing the cassock and the split bands of the Brothers of the Christian Schools. This man introduced himself as frère Marie-Victorin. We had exchanged correspondence previously, but this casual meeting was the beginning of our association. It did not last very long, for he died nine years later in 1944.

In the early years of our friendship, I was pursuing my classical studies in St-Jean and he would come on Sunday to take me out in the field. I would show him some interesting spots that I had discovered around my hometown and, little by little, we began to realize the importance of the Richelieu Valley as a migration path for several rare species of plants of southern affinity that enter Quebec along this route. Later on, he urged me to come to Montreal to study botany with him, which I did, and in 1943, I joined the staff of the Montreal Botanical Garden as a taxonomist.

He was born Conrad Kirouac in April, 1885, at Kingsey Falls, Arthabaska County, in the Eastern Townships, and was one of a family of eleven children, five of whom died in early age. He is still survived by five sisters. His family was of Breton origin with a long Canadian history, for his great-great-grandfather had emigrated to Canada in 1730.

When Conrad was still very young, his family moved to Quebec City where his father opened up a profitable grain business. He completed his first studies there and in 1901, when he was sixteen, he entered the community of the Brothers of the Christian Schools. He went through his noviciate at Mont-de-la-Salle, which was located exactly on the site where the Montreal Botanical Garden now stands. Two rows of elms, which we have preserved, date from this period.

His health was always delicate and when a physician found out that the young man was suffering from pulmonary tuberculosis, strange as it may seem, this special circumstance made a botanist out of him. He had to have a serious operation on one of his lungs—an artificial pneumothorax, to be precise. During his convalescence his superiors asked him to forget about his books and his students for a while, and to take a long rest in the healthy region of St-Jérôme, where they had a school. They suggested that he take up a hobby, and they mentioned botany.

FRÈRE MARIE-VICTORIN, É.C.

1885-1944

On a pleasant day of spring, the young Marie-Victorin was in a maple grove. He was attracted by the numerous spring-flowering plants that make our woods so lovely at this time of the year. He had a book with him, Provancher's old *Flore canadienne* (1862), but he did not know how to use it. He had in hand a specimen of *Erythronium americanum*, the Dog's-tooth Violet. Fortunately, a peasant who was passing by gave him the French vernacular name, "ail-douce" (sweet-garlic). In checking the name in the index of Provancher's book, the revelation of what a flora is came to him, how you could find the names of plants by dissections, the use of analytical keys, etc. The botanist, Marie-Victorin, was born.

Unfortunately, time does not permit us to go through all the details of his wonderful life. At that time, very few people knew about the plants in the province of Quebec, or even in Canada. He started collecting, exchanging specimens, letters, and opinions with American and European botanists, buying books on the subject, and systematically trying to explore the botanical features of his province. More important, he teamed up with a brother of his community, Brother Rolland-Germain, a Burgundian recently arrived in Canada who possessed a keen knowledge of natural history, and the two of them won recognition, both here and abroad, for the wealth of Quebec's flora.

Marie-Victorin and Rolland-Germain botanized in several regions of the Province of Quebec and even went to southern Ontario and eastern New Brunswick. But the most rewarding part of their exploratory work was probably their five trips to the Mingan–Anticosti district and to Gaspé. From 1924 to 1928, they went to the islands off the north shore of the Gulf of St-Lawrence every summer.

The Mingan Archipelago offers a strange landscape of calcareous staircases seemingly designed for giants, huge flowerpots, a weird display of fantastic gargoyles, urns, and totem-like pillars. It is also a paradise for botanists. We need only mention *Botrychium minganense*, *Cirsium minganense*, *Scirpus Rollandii*, *Solidago Victorinii*, *Solidago anticostensis*, all then new to science, not to mention the many species that had never been collected east of the Rockies, such as the beautiful *Cypripedium passerinum*.

In Gaspé, frère Marie-Victorin had a most unfortunate adventure: he fell ill and had to be carried down Mount Albert by his guides. His weak heart had once more played a trick on him. He gave up mountain-climbing but went on collecting along the various rivers that flow down from the main Gaspésian plateau to the Baie des Chaleurs. There he and Brother Rolland-Germain were rewarded by the discovery of a new Gentian and an interesting Aster, and they also brought back thousands of herbarium sheets which were distributed to various institutions.

In winter, frère Marie-Victorin would take his critical specimens to Harvard University where he submitted them to the scrutiny of his good friend Professor Fernald, the authority on the vascular flora of northeastern North America and the editor of the eighth edition of the well-known Gray's *Manual of Botany*. Together they discussed the subject of migration of plants, their isolation, and their variation.

Frère Marie-Victorin's discoveries became the subject of his technical papers and scientific communications, several of which he delivered to the Royal Society of Canada after he had been elected a fellow in 1924. At first he was in the literary French section but later he was transferred to the biology section.

His theories on the origin and evolution of the Quebec flora were presented in an important paper published in 1929, "Le dynamisme dans la flore du Québec." Fortunately for English-speaking botanists, he gave his theories a new form and reconsidered some of his earlier views in a remarkable lecture which he delivered in 1937 at the University of Notre Dame, Indiana, entitled "Phytogeographical Problems of Eastern Canada," which was published with beautiful distributional maps and illustrations in the *American Midland Naturalist* of May, 1938.

Of course, several of his theories on the phytogeography of eastern Canada are now outdated. Frère Marie-Victorin was working in the shadow of Professor Fernald and at that time the so-called "nunatak theory" reigned supreme among most northeastern American botanists. Today, we know more about the patterns of distribution of several of the rare and scanty "relics," because collecting has filled gaps. If, for example, one compares the distributional map of a given species drawn by Fernald forty years ago with those recently published by Professor Hultén, in Sweden, one soon realizes that several of these "relic" species fall into definite and well-known patterns. Nevertheless, the "nunatak theory" has been a very stimulating one and there are still some obscure Canadian species of odd and erratic distribution that are difficult to explain without it.

Frère Marie-Victorin kept a diary during most of his field trips. It is to be hoped that some day parts of it will be published in book form because they are full of noteworthy observations on remote areas and on peculiar habitats that have been either destroyed or modified, or are still not too well known botanically.

In 1920, he founded the Botanical Institute of the University of Montreal and began to train a staff to help him organize the new department. He continued to teach, lecture, and write. In addition, he launched a series of contributions for exchange with other botanical departments and for a time he was the sole contributor.

It is impossible to mention here all the titles of his bibliography. He wrote nearly one hundred papers on botanical subjects. I will mention only his monograph on Quebec ferns (1923), *Lycopodium* (1925), *Equisetum* (1926), Liliaceae (1929), Aroids (1931), his floristic studies of Temiscouata (1915), Lake St. John (1925), and Abitibi (1942).

All this culminated in 1935 in the publication of his *Flore laurentienne*—a well-illustrated and readable book even for non-botanists, which describes the plants of the upper St. Lawrence Valley. This was the first modern regional flora that included known chromosome numbers for each species. Thanks to Dr. Ernest Rouleau, a new edition of this indispensable book, in a reduced and more practical format, with an up-to-date nomenclature, and with corrections and additions, has recently been published.

Outside the botanical field, frère Marie-Victorin was a man of wide interests. He played an important role in improving the teaching of natural history at all levels through his countless articles and lectures. He made a long trip around the world, visiting various institutions and botanical gardens. While travelling in Africa, he had the good fortune of accompanying the famous Father Henri Breuil, the discoverer of the primitive paintings on the walls of the grottos of Lascaux by the Magdalenian men. In turn, this eminent priest was a good friend of a man who is highly esteemed today in intellectual circles for his stimulating views on the origin of life: the Jesuit Father Teilhard de Chardin. Through Father Breuil, frère Marie-Victorin was made aware of Chardin's new theories and he taught them to us 25 years ago at a time when several reactionary educators were afraid of the name itself: evolution.

He was a remarkable lecturer, but he was at his best during those informal gatherings when he introduced a group of us to the marvels of the flora of Quebec. Once a week, several people from various walks of life would gather in the basement of the old university on St. Denis Street and later at the Garden, each of them having in hand a copy of his *Flore laurentienne*. At the beginning of each lecture, frère Marie-Victorin would give a special "laius" as he called it. A living plant, either brought from the wild or from the greenhouse, often unusual, would be in front of him. He would tell us its history, name, use, folk-lore, etc. This description would be supplemented with slides and herbarium specimens. After that, he would open his *Flore* and lecture informally on a family, a genus, or even a single species. When the lecture was over, the students and amateurs would bring him some of their specimens either to have them named or to have their identification verified. He would name them and tell his audience whatever he knew about their occurrence, authorship, and history or recall some personal souvenir about them. The same approach was used for the botanical outings for the general public which he occasionally organized. Several of us learned from these field trips to know and like plants. Personally, I think that it is the only way to teach botany.

He founded, or had a leading hand in the founding, of societies such as the Young Naturalists Clubs, the Canadian Society of Natural History, the French-Canadian Association for the Advancement of Sciences, and he was himself a member of various botanical societies in United States and abroad.

As president of the Canadian Society of Natural History he gave a public lecture every year at which time he usually took the opportunity to discuss an important problem in botany. More often, however, he dealt with questions pertaining to education itself, for example, the teaching of natural history in the upper grades, the founding and activities of Young Naturalists Clubs, and the educational obligations of French-Canadian naturalists. He also called for the creation of an institute of geology in Quebec, a province in which the exploitation of mine resources is very important for its economy, science, and for the Canadian nation as a whole. These lectures were always beautifully written, well delivered, and largely attended. They often caused reactions in the newspapers, both pro and con. Some people of conventional views would get scared. He made himself true friends as well as important enemies. He was not only an educator of great wisdom, but a good fighter in spite of poor and failing health. His goals were high and the results he achieved worth the struggle.

In one of his lectures, delivered in 1929, he suggested that a city of the importance of Montreal urgently needed a botanical garden to educate the public by means of displays of the marvels of the vegetable kingdom. While travelling around the world, he had been impressed by beautiful botanical gardens located sometimes in very small cities. Newsmen and politicians became interested. A vigorous campaign backed him up. Work began in 1936 and, apart from the public greenhouses (these came later), the Garden was opened in 1939 to the general public and to students.

What would he say now, seeing the 200 acres nearly all planted, the nine public greenhouses, the 28 service greenhouses harbouring the third largest collection of tropical plants in the world, the 30-odd sections devoted to various perennial, economical, medicinal, alpine, and aquatic plants; specialized gardens of *Iris* and *Hemerocallis*; a test garden of annuals; children's gardens? This is not to mention an information service for the general public, distributing free leaflets on horticultural subjects; a working herbarium, a well-balanced library, an exchange service of seeds with other botanical gardens and 57 issues of a series of technical memoirs which are sent to most botanical institutions. It would indeed be a subject of pride if he were to see the thousands of visitors that come every year to see his garden.

At the time of the Garden's opening, frère Marie-Victorin was finding our Canadian winters harder and harder on him. His health was slowly deteriorating and his sleep was poor. He began to spend three to four months each winter in Cuba, where Brother Léon introduced him to the richness of the flora of the West Indies. There, he botanized, took photographs, notes, sent living material to the garden—we still grow much of it—and wrote three most interesting well-illustrated books in collaboration with Brother Léon: *Itinéraires botaniques dans l'île de Cuba.* He did not at the same time forget his friends and colleagues in Montreal. I treasure several hand-written letters from this period, full of enthusiasm for the unusual plants he was seeing and the new experiences he was having.

A l'intention des collègues et amis d'expression française, je voudrais rappeler que le frère Marie-Victorin, dont nous honorons la mémoire aujourd'hui, vingt-et-un ans après sa mort, n'a pas seulement été un botaniste éminent, fondateur de tant d'œuvres admirables qui demeurent, mais aussi un grand éducateur, un esprit profond, combatif, à qui nous devons beaucoup dans le domaine de l'enseignement et sur le plan de l'éducation. Je suis convaincu que l'actuelle révolution tranquille ne l'aurait pas effrayé, bien que la pointe d'athéisme qui l'accompagne quelquefois, l'aurait sans doute chagriné, car c'était un esprit profondément religieux.

Je voudrais rappeler ces beaux discours qu'il prononçait chaque année, alors qu'il était président de la Société canadienne d'histoire naturelle, et où les thèmes de l'enseignement des sciences et l'éducation en général étaient présentés par lui dans de nouvelles perspectives qui comblaient les uns et déconcertaient les autres. On lui en savait gré ou on lui faisait grise mine.

Je ne voudrais pas oublier non plus que le frère Marie-Victorin a joué un rôle dans nos lettres canadiennes-françaises. Sans doute, des œuvres comme les *Récits laurentiens* et les *Croquis laurentiens,* bien qu'encore de lecture charmante, sont aujourd'hui peut-être un peu dépassées.

Sa véritable action je la vois ailleurs. Par exemple, à l'occasion de la publication par l'abbé Félix-Antoine Savard, de *Menaud, maître-graveur,* il en fit, dans un discours présidentiel à l'ACFAS une longue et intelligente analyse. Le rôle qu'y jouaient la nature et particulière-ment les plantes l'émerveillait. Il en profita pour demander à nos poètes et romanciers de cesser de s'inspirer des cadres français et de la flore française, d'ailleurs empruntés aux romanciers français, et de se mettre à l'école de la route pour donner du Québec un cadre digne de ceux qui l'habitent.

On sait qu'il existe peu de races humaines véritables au sens bio-logique du mot. Mais au cours des temps, les mélanges de sangs, les brassages ethniques divers, les transhumances, migrations et guerres opèrent à la longue une sorte de sélection et finissent par grouper les individus ayant ensemble un certain nombre de souvenirs communs, d'aspirations et de désirs, développés par un certain paysage, l'absence ou la présence de la montagne ou de la mer, la couleur du ciel ou la nature du sol. C'est ainsi qu'un jour, l'individu qui incarne le mieux les qualités d'âme, les expériences ancestrales ou les aptitudes du groupement, se met à chanter ou à écrire. L'âme de ce peuple sort. Sa littérature est née.

Mais il demeure difficile à un rameau détaché du tronc français et transplanté ailleurs de vivre une aventure littéraire personnelle, tant est grande la tentation d'imiter ce qui se fait de mieux en France. C'est un peu ce qui était arrivé à nos poètes et romanciers canadiens qui ne regardaient pas la nature qui les entourait, mais empruntaient plutôt à un Bordeaux ou à un Bazin la pâleur des lis immaculés et le parfum de l'humble violette, la bruyère de la lande et la gentiane des Hautes-Alpes. Il est vrai que le gouvernement québécois nous a donné le lis candide comme fleur emblématique. Rassurez-vous : la candeur n'est que de leur côté et aussi un peu l'ignorance. J'imagine la belle colère qu'eût faite Marie-Victorin. Mais laissons ce propos.

L'auteur de la *Flore laurentienne* vit dans *Menaud, maître-graveur* une sorte de rapatriement de notre flore et il disait à ceux qu'effray-aient les noms de plantes cités par l'abbé Savard :

Mais si ces "mots", que l'on veut pourfendre, sont tout simplement les vocables vrais qui désignent des êtres qui nous entourent et que nous frôlons tout le jour sans leur demander jamais : Qui es-tu ? Alors, halte-là ! Il faut bien que quelqu'un commence à balbutier l'alphabet propre du pays laurentien ! Et si l'écrivain français peut, sans ridicule, parler de primevères et de bruyères, de thym et de marjolaine, pourquoi l'écrivain canadien craindrait-il d'appeler les choses de son pays par leur juste nom, puisqu'elles en ont un ? Pourquoi ne situerait-il pas ses personnages dans cet universel et spécifique décor de la forêt laurentienne et de ses abords, dans "ces paysages coupés de tourbières et de broussailles," parmi "les aralies et les fougères," "les kalmies enchevêtrés et gluants," le "long des sureaux rouges et des amélanchiers noirs," "des talles de harts rouges, de trembles gris-verts et des vernes dont les chatons annoncent le printemps?"

At least three books have been written on frère Marie-Victorin, a mountain range in the center of Ungava has been named after him, a boulevard travelling from Longueuil to Quebec also bears his name and it is always a shock for me when I wait for a bus at the head of Jacques-Cartier bridge to see one coming bearing the trivial information "Beaurivage—via Marie-Victorin." His monument in the Montreal Botanical Garden, the Garden itself, and of course all those species of plants either growing in Quebec or Cuba which he named or were named after him, as well as his numerous articles, essays, monographs, and books, will for centuries to come preserve the name of a great man.

J. S. ROWE

Phytogeographic Zonation: An Ecological Appreciation

TRAVELLERS OUGHT ALWAYS TO BE BOTANISTS, said Darwin, for it is the plants that everywhere give character to the landscape. The thought is happily realized in the present gathering, and increasingly its message is appropriate for all North Americans with their penchant for migrating southward in the winter, northward or to the seas and lakes in the summer, and in all directions at all seasons to attend conventions and meetings, in these perambulations frequently covering great distances and encountering striking variations in the earth's green cover.

Among botanists interest in the landscape is nurtured by a dual affection, for plants themselves and for the patterns that they form together in nature. All of us recall the pleasure of discovering beautiful wild plants; perhaps a solitary pink *Calypso* waving on the dark floor of a western larch forest, the first spring *Anemones* on a prairie hill, *Trilliums* under the green haze of leafing maples. Just as appealing, though more intellectual because more abstract, is the pattern aspect of vegetation. Some of you have come in from the far west or east, viewing from the air the intriguing designs of conifer-covered mountains, grassed valleys and plains, moss barrens, mixed evergreen-and-deciduous woodlands: a variegated landscape more and more touched with evidence of man's presence. Despite local defacement the prospect

remains ever attractive and cannot fail to stimulate interest in percep-
tive minds, raising questions about the inter-relationships of living
things, present and past, at the thin, excited interface where air and
fire meet earth and water.

Here are the two sides of phytogeography: the *floristic* with its
taxonomic and chorologic interest in the distributions and ranges of
plants, and the *vegetational* with its ecological concern for the areal
extent of plant groupings and their relationships to other geographic
phenomena. In this paper I shall consider the relationships of the two
—for both are closely related historically and conceptually—taking
examples from the forest vegetation and the tree flora with which I am
most familiar. Along the way I shall examine some perennial problems, particularly those pertaining to phytogeographic boundaries, and
finally I shall emphasize that a greater depth of focus which brings
into the picture *the total landscape* and not only its *superficial covering* opens up a more stimulating and useful prospect for those with a
bent toward phytogeography.

VEGETATION OF CANADA

First a review of the broad zonation or regionalization of Canada's
vegetation, generally pictured in a number of large divisions or "formations" which differ from one another in dominant growth forms and
in environment. These extensive landscape units or geographic ecosystems have long been known from the descriptions of such plant
geographers as Harshberger (12), Macoun and Malte (20), Weaver
and Clements (31), and Halliday (8), to mention a few. In the
following brief survey I shall follow Halliday's divisions, although
others might equally well be used.

Any description of the vegetation of this country should start with
the Boreal Forest, Canada's most widespread and typical landscape,
which extends in a broad belt from the Yukon to Newfoundland and
touches on most of the other formations. It is predominantly a coniferous forest, mossy floored or with low herbs and shrubs, interspersed
with extensive lakes and organic terrain. Fir-spruce is the typical
expression in the east, spruce-pine-aspen in the west. Northward, the
Boreal Forest grades through a subarctic savanna of lichen-woodland
and a mosaic of forest-and-tundra patches (the "hemiarctique" of
Rousseau, 26) into the arctic plains; southward, in the Prairie Provinces, it passed into the open prairie through analogous zones, the
best expressed being the mosaic aspen-and-prairie "parkland."

To the north and south of the Boreal Forest, the Tundra and the Prairie resemble one another in their treeless physiognomy. Also comparable between the two are the vegetational gradients which extend away from the Forest, in the Tundra showing a reduction in species numbers and in cover from the low to the high arctic, and in the Prairie a similar change but in the opposite direction from tall dense grassland on the north and east borders to low, sparse cover in the south and west. Just as the lowlands and sheltered places in the arctic are conspicuous as the favoured plant habitat, so are the depressions of the prairies clothed with willows and shrubby growth. River valleys that, as protected ribbons of warmth, carry Boreal Forest species far into the Tundra, function in the south as protected avenues of moistness and coolness, allowing penetration of many of the same species deep into the plains.

The Subalpine Forest in the southern two-thirds of British Columbia and the adjacent highlands of Alberta is the mountain counterpart of the Boreal Forest; indeed, it has recently become almost consanguinous thanks to the activities of taxonomists (Boivin, 2, and Taylor, 30) who propose to treat *Abies lasiocarpa* as a subspecies of *Abies balsamea*, and *Picea engelmannii* as a subspecies of *Picea glauca*. However, lodgepole pine (*Pinus contorta latifolia*) has so far maintained its specific identity apart from jack pine (*P. Banksiana*), and the formation is also distinguished by the relative unimportance of poplars, birches, and black spruce (*Picea mariana*), as well as by a unique western flora.

The temperate coniferous Coast Forest along the mild Pacific shore has a counterpart too: the Columbia Forest of the interior "wet belt." Each consists of a matrix of western hemlock (*Tsuga heterophylla*), cedar (*Thuja plicata*), and Douglas fir (*Pseudotsuga menziesii*); but the Coast Forest, in addition to its more massive trees which reflect a particularly favourable milieu, is typified by a number of distinctive companion species, such as Sitka spruce (*Picea sitchensis*) and amabilis fir (*Abies amabilis*). In turn, the Columbia Forest has its own complement of characteristic species, for example the western larch (*Larix occidentalis*).

A fourth Cordilleran landscape is the Plateau Montane Forest of British Columbia, lying in the rain shadow of the high coastal and interior mountains. It severely tests easy descriptions of "formations," for into its composition enter species that by association, and perhaps too glibly, are designated as Boreal (*Picea glauca*), Subalpine (*Abies lasiocarpa*), Coastal (*Pseudotsuga menziesii*, the inland variety), and

Columbian (*Larix occidentalis*). Only in the southern part has it a unique dominant, the ponderosa pine (*Pinus ponderosa*).

Crossing the continent, the Deciduous Forest of southern Ontario stands out as a distinctive formation, with its summer-moist climate, its low content of evergreens, and its mixture of mesophytic species in which oaks, hickories, ashes, and other broad-leaved "hardwoods" are richly represented. Between it and the Boreal Forest appears the Great Lakes–St. Lawrence Forest and farther east the similar Acadian Forest in the Maritime Provinces. Formerly, an assumed fidelity of red spruce (*Picea rubens*) to the Atlantic region suggested recognition of the Acadian Forest as a separate formation, but now its main support is the wedge of *terra incognita* (the State of Maine) intruding from the south, a blank area on the map that creates a neat discontinuity! As in the British Columbia Montane Forest, a mixture of life-forms and species complicates categorization of the Great Lakes–St. Lawrence–Acadian landscape. The simple solution is to designate it as "transitional between Boreal and Deciduous Forests." Here is a good place to examine more closely the relationship between a particular vegetation zone and the species that characterize it.

FORMATIONS AND SPECIES

This general landscape in which at Ottawa we find ourselves, the Great Lakes–St. Lawrence Forest, has attracted the interest of many students. One of the best known is Nichols (22) who at first interpreted the vegetation as an intermediate between the Deciduous and the Boreal evergreen (taiga) formations but later revised his opinion and proposed a separate formation: the "Hemlock–White Pine–Northern Hardwood Forest," or more briefly the "Eastern Hemlock Forest" from its most typical member. Reviewing earlier studies he pointed out that four or five important trees are practically confined to the region (hemlock, white pine, yellow birch, red pine, and "perhaps red spruce") and that several others obviously belonged by virtue of having their centres of north-south distribution within the region or immediately to the south of it (sugar maple, basswood, and northern red oak). Some obvious difficulties were recognized, such as the necessity of making a place in the "climax" for species which, though prominent here, are even more so in the north (balsam fir and white spruce) and in the south (beech, elm, and white ash), but presumably as a counterbalance Nichols pointed out that many other species important to the north and south were *not* present!

To illustrate the centre or "core" of the formation, Nichols superimposed the ranges of the four "endemic" tree species, and those of three
other distinctive trees, thus revealing "the eastern hemlock region as
the area of greatest concentration for the two groups of trees concerned." Note the circularity; the region having been identified by a
particular complement of species is then revealed as the area of
greatest concentration of them. One looks in vain for a discussion of
boundaries; Nichols' maps show no exact coincidence between ranges
of the key species, nor between formation boundaries and species
range boundaries.

The question of boundaries is raised in no spirit of narrow or carp-
ing criticism but to illustrate an essential point relevant to all areal
"units" of vegetation, viz., that description and classification, in terms
of particular combinations and abundances of species at centres of
area, is easy and appealing, but bounding the "units" is not. The
reason is a floristic one: every species while sharing area with others
has its unique pattern of prominence and distribution. Therefore each
"core" of overlapped species, described in terms of the presence and
prominence of the juxtaposed plants, has theoretically as many possible
boundaries as there are species. Cores can be typified in general terms
but boundary lines demand attention to particulars, unless of course
they simply split the difference between adjacent cores and are pur-
posely left vague.

Gilmour and Walters (5) have recently contrasted two kinds of
classification: the "typological," based on general family resemblances
but vague as to boundaries, and the "definitional," based on specific
criteria. Vegetation lends itself better to the former than to the latter,
and not without reason is the classification of vegetation sometimes
called "typology." As is often the case, the two possible approaches
appeal to different kinds of minds, exemplified today by the confronta-
tion of those students of vegetation satisfied with general composi-
tional similarities and those demanding exactitude, of those who select
and sample cores and those who search for boundaries and find only
gradients of varying steepness, of those who typify and those who
ordinate as a means of sharpening the definition of their stand samples.

In parenthesis, an understanding of classification and particularly
of its purposive nature would long ago have solved some of the major
disagreements pertaining to vegetation and its taxonomy. Gleason (6),
much quoted by anti-typologists, has suggested that "a precisely
logical classification of stands of vegetation is impossible because no
two communities are precisely alike," a statement that can be
interpreted as meaning that no two communities are sufficiently alike

to meet *his* rigid definitional standards. A pertinent aspect that has not, so far as I know, been explored is that relating classifiability to the *scale* at which vegetation is viewed. If a large and complex geographic area is divided and subdivided again and again, the possibilities for establishing a "precisely logical classification" are increased with each division which reduces the scale of the differences between units. Indeed, Gleason (6) admitted that similar vegetation did occur within a limited space, i.e., on small contiguous areas; he rested his argument for the individuality of communities by reference to the broad regional scene. In brief, those whose sample areas are large will inevitably discover uniqueness; those whose sample areas are small, numerous, and in the same vicinity are more apt to discover that essential of classification, *acceptable* alikeness.

To return to boundaries: the problem is, of the many possible boundaries are some "better" than others? Much depends on presuppositions of importance; what seems meaningful to one may not seem so to another.

Where vegetational life-form changes abruptly, as where forest meets prairie, there seems to be a "natural" boundary—especially if it is thought to be statically fixed. On the other hand, in areas of broad and gradual transition the element of human decision in setting boundaries is obvious; for example, the placing of the line between the Boreal and Subarctic forest vegetations where 10 per cent or 50 per cent of the surface bears lichen-woodland (Hare and Taylor, 10). Between these extremes are the many boundaries which, partly depending on scale, appear to represent something more than chance; for example, the northern edge of the Deciduous formation in southern Ontario where a dozen or so "Carolinian" broad-leaved trees and numerous minor plants reach approximately the same limit (Soper, 29), or the southern edge of the Boreal formation marked in the east by the range limits of such trees as red pine, white pine, and red oak (the "limes labradoricus" or southern "main tree-line" of Hustich, 14).

Some of the problems of boundary significance are illuminated by a consideration of the ranges of plants and of the reasons why they are where they are. Let us next examine two influences—migration history and fire—in relation to floristic phytogeography.

SPECIES RANGES AND MIGRATION

Taking a large view of the country and using the native tree flora as a yardstick, it is apparent that in Canada there are two centres of species richness: southern British Columbia with a preponderance of conifers, and southern Ontario with a preponderance of broad-leaved trees. From these centres, numbers of species decrease toward the centre of the country and from south to north. For example, in approximate figures there are 30 tree species in British Columbia, 20 in Alberta (including the Rockies), and 10 in Saskatchewan. In southern Ontario there are perhaps 75 native tree species, with about 50 at the latitude of Ottawa and Montreal, half this number (25) in the Clay Belt, and again half as many (12) near James Bay.

These gradients of decreasing numbers of species parallel, to some extent, gradients of decreasing environmental favourability, but more than this they reflect differing abilities to migrate rapidly, to compete, and to adapt during the relatively short period that the land has been exposed since the Ice Age.

The glaciated surface of Canada is young, opened in the last 10,000 years or so to invasion. As a general and somewhat oversimplified picture, the species present in the far north—white spruce, black spruce, tamarack, birch, poplar, willows—are the "weeds," the fast travellers, with light, wind-borne or water-borne seeds. Small-fruited genera such as *Prunus* and *Sorbus* have doubtless been carried into the subarctic by birds. In lower latitudes many species are larger seeded, slower migrators; the pines, maples, basswood, for example. Farthest south are the large-seeded trees: the oaks, hickories, walnut, butternut, distributed by animals at a still slower pace. Godwin (7) has discussed the palynological evidence of such differential tree migration in the British Isles, pointing out that the trees dominating the lowest pollen zones, the birch and pine, are light-seeded plants capable of quicker spread than the heavy-seeded elements of the mixed-oak forest of the later zones. Drury's (4) analogy is pertinent: "The great vegetation zones of the north are perhaps best thought of as temporarily exaggerated in their segregation, as though in a great natural experiment resembling paper chromatography."

Two points are worth noting. One is that the surficial materials, newly exposed immediately after the recession of ice and water, were not inimical to the invasion of many plants. In the vicinity of Ottawa today the "raw" mineral soils exposed by gully-erosion of the Champlain Sea clays are rapidly colonized by spruce, cedar, hemlock, white pine, aspen, and birch. It may be that the fresh, unweathered soils, permeable and lacking the clay pan structures that developed later by weathering and leaching, provided the optimum rooting medium for a host of upland species that streamed northward with or ahead of the light-seeded conifers and intolerant broad-leaved trees. The second point is the manifest speed with which the invasion must have taken place. Spruce in the Keewatin District, more than a thousand miles from the nearest unglaciated refugia, presumably averaged a rate of at least a mile every ten years (3 or 4 miles per generation) in order to reach that area today. The abilities displayed to travel without mycorrhizal symbionts, and to acclimatize rapidly to changing day-length and temperature during this long trip, raise important questions that cannot be explored here.

The initial surge of invasion by species that favour open soils must have been succeeded by a phase of competition and partial or total elimination as the dominants consolidated their cover and as soils weathered and changed in nutrient regime and in moisture retentivity. Perhaps the various patches of prairie found deep within the northern and eastern formations can be explained as relicts of a much earlier and wider spread. However, where the first invaders were *tree* species, themselves dominating life-forms, the process of elimination and replacement must have proceeded comparatively slowly. Eastern white cedar (*Thuja occidentalis*) around Hudson Bay and red pine (*Pinus resinosa*) in Newfoundland may be examples of species whose ranges have been considerably reduced by more aggressive competitors. But the northernmost trees have held their own. After all, the major factor in competition is getting there first, of pre-empting space in soil and air, and by that pre-emption excluding later arrivals. Once the Boreal species invaded and took over the north they perforce limited to the south the slower travellers' ranges.

There is a tendency to accept the present distributions of species as fixed, nicely adjusted in a state of equilibrium, possessing therefore a special significance that awaits discovery in relation to soil or to climate. For example, the species that we call "Boreal" seem to belong naturally in the cold north. Surprise is natural when fossil parts of white spruce and tamarack are discovered in Pleistocene sediments in the southern States—evidence that they grew some 800 miles south of their present limits—and a climatic and zonal displacement is immediately postulated. Zoologists are tougher-minded: the bones of elephants and bears in southern Saskatchewan are not interpreted as indicating former tropical and montane climates, but as meaning that mammoths and grizzlies once roamed there, adapted to a climate not unlike the present one, and that these particular ecotypes disappeared. We cannot imagine what vegetation patterns would prevail if, without climatic change, the surface of Canada were to remain ice free for 10,000 years more, but it is certain that the ranges of species and the consequent phytogeographic zonation would not remain as they are today.

One of the important environmental determinants of the ranges of species is fire, either acting directly to eliminate plants or indirectly to clear the ground of established cover and initiate a new cycle of immigration and competition. Almost all the native vegetation of Canada shows the influence of fire.

The Boreal Forest is the "fire forest" *par excellence*, at least in most of its parts. While its regional diversity appears to depend primarily on the moisture retentivity of the soils, the effects of frequency and intensity of fires (related to regularity of the precipitation pattern during the spring-to-autumn season) clearly exerts an additional control. Selection has been for species that can sprout or disseminate seed widely following burning. The basic pattern shows a dominance on the well-drained sites by balsam fir in Newfoundland and along the Quebec north shore, changing to the dominance of white spruce in Manitoba and westward, with black spruce and tamarack forming the forests on peats, and jack pine usually on excessively drained soils except in the extreme east where it is absent. Inextricably woven into the pattern are the effects of fires which in the east favour black spruce, birch, and jack pine over balsam fir, and in the west give the advantage to aspen, jack pine, black spruce, and birch over white spruce. Northward the Boreal belt is dominated by black spruce, reflecting both the increase in frequency of wet peaty substrata and the prevalence of fire. Southward where irregular rainfall also sets the stage for fire, the soils are better drained and black spruce is unimportant compared to jack pine, aspen, and white spruce. A "mass effect" in regeneration should be noted, whereby species present in abundance before disturbance are at an advantage in extending their distributions afterward; this explains the tendency in areas of extensive peaty lowlands, especially in the north, for black spruce to dominate the upland sites following repeated fires.

The impress of fire can also be seen in most of the other formations; even in the Deciduous Forest it has doubtless played a role in perpetuating, for example, the oaks. In the Great Lakes–St. Lawrence–Acadian Forest the prominence of evergreens, especially the characteristic red pine and white pine, can be traced to fire history. The typical coniferous expression of the Cordilleran forests shows fire control, as would be expected in the summer-dry west. Even the "wet" Pacific coast forests burn periodically, and Schmidt (28) has shown conclusively that the distribution of Douglas fir, altitudinally and latitudinally, is directly related to this form of disturbance.

Perhaps most instructive are the southern and northern boundaries of the Boreal Forest in west-central Canada, where there is strong evidence that the positions of the tree-lines are set by fire. That this is so for the forest-prairie boundary can hardly be doubted. In competition with woody vegetation, grass lands are maintained and extended by repeated fires, and Bird (1) has documented both the history of burning and the southward shift of the forest when, at the beginning of the century, agricultural development reduced the incidence of fires in the Canadian west. Just where the southern tree-line would stabilize itself in the absence of fire is not known, but there are some, such as Wells (32), who suggest that the forest, now confined within the grasslands to valleys and to relatively fire-proof rock outcrops, scarps, and sandhill crests, would engulf the prairie. A forest formation of *Populus, Picea, Quercus, Pinus, Juniperus,* and *Celtis* where now the cereals and native grasses wave is an intriguing but not farfetched idea. Incidentally, acceptance of the important role of fire within the forest casts a different light on forest "stability." The stable parts are the topographically "fire proof" loci—open sand hills, rock ridges, and wet lands.

And what of the northern forest boundary, the arctic tree-line? Students of the subarctic mention the prevalence of fire; e.g., Lutz (18), Hare and Taylor (10), Hustich (15), but there is less mention of it in the arctic. This may only mean that, as in other treeless vegetation such as the southern grassland, fire leaves few conspicuous traces. Ritchie (24) pointed out that at least some of the "tundra" vegetation within the forest-tundra transition in northern Manitoba occupied sites where fire had removed the tree cover, and indeed the prominent life-forms of the north—graminoid and ericoid—are strongly suggestive of fire history. Man has not lacked an incentive to burn the tundra and subarctic forests as Lutz (19) has shown, and man using fire has been on this continent for at least 30,000 years. Discovery of tree remains north of the present tree-line are usually taken to indicate a climatic deterioration and a retreat of the forest southward, but when the remains include charred wood (Bryson *et al.*, 3), it may not be necessary to invoke the palaeoecologist's *deus ex machina*, climatic change.

Where species of similar growth forms are mixed together it is difficult to observe evidences of instability. The popularity among geobotanists of "timber-lines" on mountains, and of "tree-lines" at the edges of tundra and of prairie, stems from the ease with which individuals of the arboreal species, conspicuously outlined against a vegetation of different life-form, can be accurately located and studied. This does not, however, confer greater "significance" on the conspicuous "tree-lines" than on the thousands of other plant range limits that lie hidden from view in the matrix of a more homogeneous vegetation. There are at least 75 tree-lines in Ontario, each one as significant or insignificant as the next. What the conspicuous tree-lines do show of importance is that species' ranges are actively changing today, and not in response to climatic change. There is no reason to believe that the observable disequilibrium is unique or even rare; probably all species are shifting this way and that, at different speeds determined by opportunity and by rate of evolutionary change.

The conclusion is that the ranges of plants frequently reflect a chance history of migration related to the vagaries of opportunity, competition, and disturbances such as fire. Similarly, vegetation—the observable areal aggregations of plants—contains an element of chance, and expresses in its more or less haphazard groupings the continuing, dynamic evolution and migration of plants. Therefore it is a mistake to look for close relationships between plant distributions and climate or soils.

PHYTOGEOGRAPHY AND CLIMATE

A favourite pastime of phytogeographers is seeking the climatic determinants of the ranges of plants and of the zonations of vegetation. The idea that climate exerts the master control over the distribution of the various forms of earth life is rarely challenged because it seems so plausible. It is a matter of experience that proceeding north or south, up to the high lands or down to the low, the patterns of vegetation change and so obviously does climate. Also, we turn the pages of our atlases and find that climatic boundaries do indeed match vegetational boundaries (the atlases do not report the extent to which climatologists and botanists use each other's maps). Furthermore, because "climate" is an abstract category, comprehending a mixed bag of inter-related factors which impinge on or act over the earth's surface, it has a satisfying capacity to explain everything. When one parameter is tried and found wanting, for example, "temperature" as used by

Merriam (21) to bound the North American life-zones, another one appears in its place, for example, "thermal efficiency" as used by Hare (9) to bound the Boreal subzones in Quebec-Labrador.

Plants are infinitely variable, adapting by ecotypic differentiation to a spectrum of environments. Common sense tells us that a *Picea–Larix* stand in Ungava exists in a different climate than a *Picea–Larix* stand in the Yukon or a *Picea–Larix* stand in southern Manitoba, and that if climate "controls" all three then climate has no sharp meaning. But beyond this fuzziness in concept there is a basic fallacy in climatic determinism; the distributions of plants and of plant aggregations depend not only on climate but also, as previously pointed out, on history and on physiography, on the age of the land and the nature of its surface, on opportunities for migration, on competition and disturbances. Ecological studies have amply demonstrated that the controls over plant distributions are both ecosystematic and historical; all lesser apparent controls are coincidental.

The converse is also true; phytogeographic boundaries do *not* mark climatic boundaries. To map climates on the basis of vegetation is illogical; vegetation zones are vegetation zones, not bioclimatic zones. Just as illogical is the attempt to define "natural" regional boundaries on the basis of former vegetation patterns, traced out with painstaking labour through study of old surveys and other historical records. To reconstruct the vegetation as it used to be 100, 200, or 1,000 years ago may have various values, but a better understanding of the potential of the land, or of presumed "natural" climatic or soil boundaries, is not among them. To go back in time is not necessarily to find greater stability, a more perfect fit of vegetation to climate and soils, but perhaps less. Instability in nature is a fact that must be recognized (Raup, 23); it is a tragedy that such an untidy fact should have dispatched the neat theory of "climax."

PHYTOGEOGRAPHY AND LANDFORM

The main problems of phytogeography relate to range limits and vegetational boundaries. From the vast and complex patterns of plant cover on the land surface, vegetational units of various sizes can be identified according to purpose and the scale appropriate to each purpose. Using the formations as examples, I have suggested that vegetation can be *typified* with ease in terms of characteristic species visible at the "core" but *bounded* with difficulty due to its aggregate nature.

Further, when the various floristic boundaries are examined it is found that they are frequently haphazard, related indirectly if at all to the limitations of specific environmental factors, and casting in doubt the popular assumption of close correlation between climate and the geographic positions of either individual species or of communities of species.

What then *can* be inferred where clear vegetational boundaries, i.e., coincidences of distributions or ranges of species, do appear? The explanation may relate to the vagaries of migration, groups of species having travelled at approximately the same rate of speed to reach a certain line in space at the same time. Or a dominant life-form may bring along with it a group of dependent species, the limits of the dominant then marking a distinct vegetational boundary. Or again, a line separating dissimilar vegetational communities may mark the limits of a past disturbance, such as fire or insect attack. However, there is one kind of vegetational boundary of broad significance, thereby rating the epithet "natural"; it is the boundary that is aligned with a physiographic boundary, a change in "landform" (the term being here used to include geological composition and structure as well as form of the earth's surface layer).

Landform is the basic component of the landscape, the "parent" of the soil developed below its surface and of the topoclimate developed above, selecting and controlling, through its control of soil and local climate, the composition and structure of the community of living things that inhabits it. Therefore any sharp limits of landform units always mark actual or potential boundaries of soils, climate, and vegetation. Conversely, soil and vegetation may indicate where biologically significant boundaries between intergrading landforms should be placed. The ecological importance of landform suggests one answer to the problem of dividing up the frequently diffuse, erratic, or fluctuating patterns of plant cover, namely, to relate the vegetation and its boundaries to landforms and their boundaries. This exercise, which may be called "grounding" the vegetation, is guaranteed to give it a substantiality and meaning otherwise lacking. There are sound theoretical reasons for this assertion.

The landscape is an ecological system and can be conceived as a pattern of intergrading ecosystem units, each terrestrial one consisting of an earth layer (landform-soil and its biota) plus a superimposed air layer (climate and the visible plant and animal community). Every ecosystem unit or land unit is an open but functional system. Vegetation on the other hand is no system; it is a component, a class based on common occupancy of the ecosystem "box," lacking functional relations save through the ecosystem's two layers—land and air—in which its member plants are embedded. This is the basis for the assertion that "vegetation has no physiology and is therefore an incomplete and unsatisfactory object of scientific study" (Rowe, 27), even though it has spatial attributes which allow its description and classification. In other words, the study of vegetational phytogeography—or in even broader terms, the study of biotic communities as communities and not as ecosystems—has limited value, fascinating though it may be.

The ecosystem concept is popular today but unassimilated. Many ecologists, I regret to say, tip their hats to it and return to a scholastic phytosociology. "Too difficult to apply," runs the argument, and certainly its application requires a widening of interest beyond plants and vegetation to other geographic disciplines. The possibilities, however, are indicated by several geobotanical reconnaissances of northern Canada made in recent years, strongly oriented to the vegetation but with ecosystematic overtones: the study and mapping of Labrador–Ungava by Hare (11) and his associates at McGill University, and the study and mapping of northern Manitoba by Ritchie (25) at the University of Manitoba. In both studies a broad interest in the geographic landscape is expressed, with concurrent attention to plant cover and to landform; both studies demonstrate the importance and ecological significance of physiographic boundaries.

The synthesis of vegetation and landform is perhaps best expressed and carried to its logical end in the landscape classifications developed by foresters in Canada, for example by Hills (13) with recent examples by Jurdant (16) and Lacate (17). The methods rely on use of aerial photographs to survey the landscape, matching the patterns of vegetation and landform to define morphological land units of consistent geological structure, topography, soils, and vegetation. In this, phytogeography plays an important though not dominant role, making a contribution both to land classification and to interpretations of potential land use.

In conclusion, the subject of phytogeographic zonation raises problems relating to the distributions of plant species and to coincidences of their ranges. Boundaries between different vegetational areas are rarely presented in nature with satisfying precision, and an understanding of geographical history and of plant ecology shows why this is necessarily so. Man sets boundaries to geographic phenomena according to purpose and appropriate scale; choice and a sense of importance are implicit in the lines that he draws on maps. As "vegetation" is an abstract concept compared to the substantiality of the landscape ecosystem, units of the former and their boundaries will be especially significant if related to the latter.

A noted geographer recently remarked that geographers in general are not habituated to the idea of being useful, and presumably phyto-geographers are no exception. Nevertheless, being useful has its virtues, and phytogeography in the context of "ecosystemology"—of landscape study, inventory, and land management—can look ahead to a virtuous and meaningful future.

REFERENCES

1. BIRD, R. D. 1961. Ecology of the aspen parkland. Can. Dept. Agr. Res. Br. Publ. 1066.
2. BOIVIN, B. 1959. *Abies balsamea* (Linné) Miller et ses variations. Nat. Can. *86*: 219–223.
3. BRYSON, R. A., W. N. IRVING, and J. A. LARSEN. 1965. Radiocarbon and soil evidence of former forest in the southern Canadian Tundra. Science, *147*: 46–48.
4. DURY, W. H. 1956. Bog flats and physiographic processes in the upper Kuskokwim River Region, Alaska. Contr. Gray Herb. No. 178.
5. GILMOUR, J. S. L., and S. M. WALTERS. 1964. Philosophy and classifica-tion. *In* W. B. TURRILL, ed., Vistas in Botany *4*: 1–22.
6. GLEASON, H. A. 1939. The individualistic concept of the plant association. Am. Midl. Nat. *21*: 92–108.
7. GODWIN, H. 1956. The History of the British Flora. Cambridge Univ. Press. 384 pp.
8. HALLIDAY, W. E. D. 1937. A forest classification for Canada. Forest Ser-vice Bull. *89*: Can. Dept. Mines and Resources.
9. HARE, F. K. 1950. Climate and zonal divisions of the boreal forest forma-tion in eastern Canada. Geograph. Rev. *40*: 615–635.
10. —— 1959. A photo-reconnaissance survey of Labrador–Ungava. Memoir 6, Geograph. Br. Dept. Mines and Tech. Surv., Ottawa.
11. Hare, F. K., and R. G. Taylor. 1956. The position of certain forest boundaries in southern Labrador–Ungava. Geograph. Bull. No. 8, Can. Dept. Mines and Tech. Surv.
12. HARSHBERGER, J. W. 1911. Phytogeographic Survey of North America. G. E. Stechert & Co., New York. 790 pp.
13. HILLS, G. A. 1961. The ecological basis for land-use planning. Ont. Dept. Lands and Forests, Res. Rept. No. 46. 204 pp.
14. HUSTICH, I. 1949. On the forest geography of the Labrador Peninsula: A preliminary synthesis. Acta Geographica *10*: 1–63.
15. —— 1957. On the phytogeography of the subarctic Hudson Bay lowland. Acta Geographica *16*: 1–48.
16. JURDANT, M. 1964. Photo interpretation and forest land classification. Woodlands Rev. Sec., Pulp and Paper Mag. of Canada, Oct. 1964. Forest Res. Br., Contr. No. 634.
17. LACATE, D. S. 1965. Forest land classification for the University of British Columbia Research Forest. Forest Res. Br., Dept. of Forestry, Publ. No. 1107.

18. LUTZ, H. J. 1956. Ecological effects of forest fires in the interior of Alaska. U.S.D.A., Tech. Bull. No. 1133.
19. ——— 1959. Aboriginal man and white man as historical causes of fires in the boreal forest, with particular reference to Alaska. Yale Univ. School of Forestry, Bull. No. 65.
20. MACOUN, J. M., and M. O. MALTE. 1917. The flora of Canada. Can. Dept. of Mines. Geol. Surv. Mus. Bull. No. 26, 14 pp.
21. MERRIAM, C. H. 1898. Life zones and crop zones of the United States. U.S.D.A., Div. Biol. Surv., Bull. No. 10: 9–79.
22. NICHOLS, G. E. 1935. The hemlock–white pine–northern hardwood region of eastern North America. Ecology 16: 403–422.
23. RAUP, H. M. 1964. Some problems in ecological theory and their relation to conservation. J. Ecol. 52 (Suppl.): 19–28.
24. RITCHIE, J. C. 1960. The vegetation of northern Manitoba: IV, The Caribou Lake Region. Can. J. Botany 38: 185–199.
25. ——— 1962. A geobotanical survey of Northern Manitoba. Arctic Institute of North America, Tech. Pap. No. 9: 1–46.
26. ROUSSEAU, J. 1952. Les zones biologiques de la Péninsule Québec–Labrador et l'hémiarctique. Can. J. Botany 30: 436–474.
27. ROWE, J. S. 1961. The level-of-integration concept and ecology. Ecology 42: 420–427.
28. SCHMIDT, R. L. 1960. Factors controlling the distribution of Douglas fir in coastal British Columbia. Quart. J. Forestry 54: 156–160.
29. SOPER, J. H. 1955. Some families of restricted range in the Carolinian flora of Canada. Trans. Roy. Can. Inst. 31: 69–90.
30. TAYLOR, T. M. C. 1959. The taxonomic relationship between Picea glauca (Moench) Voss., and Picea engelmannii Parry. Madrono 15: 111–115.
31. WEAVER, J. E., and F. E. CLEMENTS. 1929. Plant Ecology. McGraw-Hill Book Co. Inc., New York. 520 pp.
32. WELLS, P. V. 1965. Scarp woodlands, transported grassland soils, and concept of grassland climate in the great plains region. Science 148: 246–249.

HOWARD CRUM

Evolutionary and Phytogeographic Patterns in the Canadian Moss Flora

THE CANADIAN FLORA is an accident of its climatic and geological history. It is an abstraction, difficult to define or analyze because of a diversity of content and origin and also because of unnatural boundaries imposed by political compromise, convenience, and tradition. It is many floras, or parts of many floras, inter-related and interdigitated. The evolution of the bryoflora is a many-sided topic for discussion, fundamentally difficult because the country is huge, bryophytes are numerous, and bryologists are few. Very little is known about the evolution of bryophytes, in Canada or elsewhere. Even their origin from more primitive plants is a matter for conjecture and debate. Studies in developmental morphology, cytology, and paleontology have been too scattered and too fragmentary to be of much use, and phytogeographic evidence of origin and migration is limited by a scarcity of taxonomic information on relationships of species elsewhere in the world.

It would seem that evolution at the specific level is at a near standstill. Mosses and liverworts are extremely ancient, but even the oldest fossils or humified remains of bryophytes are, for the most part, similar, if not identical to modern species. There are very few endemic genera or species in the Canadian flora, and such as there are may be discovered, on further investigation, to be outside the political limits of the country as well. A good share of them are segregates from generic or specific complexes, representing, after all, personal opinions subject to re-interpretation. Although numerous regional races, varieties, or subspecies clutter up the literature and add to the burden of the taxonomist, the amplitude of genetic and environmental variation is too poorly understood to admit such deviants as compelling evidence of progressive genetic change rather than symptoms of ecological abnormality.

Owing to the turbulence of its physiographic and climatic history, the vastness of Canada has not been available to its present flora until relatively recent times. After the final retreat of Pleistocene ice, the country was no doubt colonized by species of adaptability and aggressiveness. A high percentage of Canadian bryophytes are taxonomically difficult because of their great variability and it is tempting to think of such troublemakers as genetically plastic and evolutionary dynamic—as youthful species on the march—as compared with the old, genetically stable, and less migratory species of ancient floras. This may indeed be true in some instances, but many of our most troublesome mosses, like the many species of *Drepanocladus* and other Amblystegiaceae, are aquatics or semi-aquatics which vary during the growing season with changing water levels and alkalinity or species of wide range, like *Hylocomium splendens*, occurring, for example, in stunted forms in the marginal environments of the arctic or particularly lush forms in the optimum conditions of the Pacific Coast.

Examples of specialization and adaptive radiation into ecospecies are easily found. *Dicranum bergeri* of open peat bogs is obviously related to *D. drummondii* of rather moist coniferous forests, and *D. fuscescens* of mesic woodland sites becomes *D. condensatum* in drier woods and *D. spurium* in open, sandy habitats. The differences between such ecospecies are not particularly impressive in the extreme, and they are often non-existent in intergrading forms, thus indicating only slight genetic separation. Most bryophytes are adapted to fairly specific conditions of shade, moisture, and pH. Some grow only on trees, others on rocks. Some of the Splachnaceae grow on the dung of carnivores, some of the dung of herbivores. Some of our most interesting mosses are minute ephemerals which complete their short life cycles in the early spring or late fall when competition from larger plants is at a minimum. And many of our most curious species are pioneers of recently disturbed situations. They are also short-cycle plants, living in habitats later dominated by weeds, but they are by no means weedy or cosmopolitan in distribution. Although disturbed habitats have been increasingly numerous because of man's extended activities in recent years, the mosses typical of such habitats, unlike *Crataegus*, show no signs of evolutionary explosion.

In most or all the cases of ecological specialization mentioned here, broad distributions and, frequently, wide disjunctions in familiar patterns suggest that we are not dealing with recent evolution, but with ancient variants already widespread in times of phytogeographic antiquity, unless we seek the less likely explanation of parallel evolution in widely separated areas. Polytopic evolution of identical species is no doubt possible, but it puts a strain on credulity to use polytopic origins too often in explaining the broken ranges of species or even minor variants of species.

Owing to the paucity and uncertainty of other evidence, the origin of the Canadian flora can be inferred only from an investigation of distributions. No one working with the taxonomy or floristics of bryophytes needs to be told that bryophytes occupy natural ranges predetermined by historical factors. Although phanerogamic botanists generally assume that spore-bearing plants are diffusely and ubiquitously distributed, phytogeographic and monographic studies have demonstrated that, in spite of random, long-range dispersal of spores, pteridophytes, hepatics, mosses, and lichens are governed in their ranges by ecological and historical factors and are distributed in much the same patterns as the seed plants. As a result, phytogeographic conclusions drawn from the distributions of phanerogams can be tested and strengthened by the distributions of cryptogams.

Most bryophytes have fairly definite environmental requirements and are accordingly limited to ecological associations where those requirements are met. The possibility of successful migration over long distances is minimized by the off-chance that a spore will fall into exactly the right habitat at the right time for growth and can overcome competition from native species suited to the same habitat. The difficulties of invading closed associations seem prohibitive, and open disturbed situations are usually quickly occupied by species with broad ecological tolerance and short life cycles, or both. Although there are many widespread, weedy bryophytes and many ephemerals too, disturbed habitats are unsuitable for most mosses and certainly for most species of phytogeographic significance. Even if a chance immigrant could live in such a disturbed situation, vigorous natives, already present in force, would have the advantage of numbers. Many widely distributed bryophytes, such as *Rhytidium rugosum*, rarely produce spores and have no known means of vegetative reproduction (except for the slow process of tuft formation from a budding protonema). Although it is hard to understand how such species became widely distributed, their ranges can scarcely be attributed to long-range dispersal. In the case of dioecious species without some means of vegetative reproduction, successful colonization would depend on the unlikely establishment of both male and female strains in proximity at the same time.

The improbability of long-range dispersal does not, of course, rule out its possibility. It is indeed difficult to explain otherwise the biotic occupation of remote oceanic islands of sudden volcanic origin, such as the Hawaiian Islands. It should be noted, however, that the possibilities for chance introduction of waifs and strays from distant lands are infinitely greater on such newly formed and isolated areas offering a variety of habitats and a minimum of competition than on an old continental land mass where the ecological niches have long since been filled.

The literature on the efficacy of long-range dispersal is extensive. Arguments for the chance introduction of various groups of plants and animals of remote origin are ably presented by Zimmerman (23), and Wulff (22) reviewed the case for the slow, step-wise migration which probably obtains under ordinary conditions; a complete résumé of dispersal problems was recently presented by Skottsberg (15). Although long-range dispersal is freely admitted as a possibility, it seems probable that both phanerogams and cryptogams generally spread slowly from a centre of origin or dispersal and that the size and shape of their areas will be determined by past and present conditions of climate and geology and also by the inherent ability of the species to invade new territories and adjust to changing conditions.

Modern distributions often provide a clue to the history of a flora. A similar origin and history of migration may be suggested by a number of genera or species occupying similarly discontinuous areas, but in the case of specific disjuncts, the possibility of recent, chance introduction must be borne in mind. A high degree of specific differentiation in the various parts of a dissected generic range suggests a long history of evolution since the primary generic dispersal. On the other hand, a large group of identical species of similar disjunction may indicate a continuity of area too recent for appreciable evolutionary change. For the most part, species of mosses occur in the same patterns of disjunction as those occupied by genera of higher plants. Such specific disjunctions would in themselves be of little interest or significance, except by sheer force of numbers, unless it were granted that bryophytes are very ancient and have evolved so slowly that specific disjunctions among them are equivalent to generic disjunctions among more rapidly evolving higher plants.

The history of any bryoflora is obscured by a dearth of information on the age and origin of the group. Morphologically, bryophytes are obviously primitive, and their ancestral origins are lost in antiquity. Certainly there has been considerable phylogenetic divergence between the Hepaticae and the Musci, and in the Musci, the Sphagnobrya, Andreaeobrya, and Eubrya are only remotely related. Many families of the Eubrya seem surprisingly distinct for such a relatively small group. Other evidence of antiquity is provided by the fact that most genera of bryophytes are very widely distributed and are represented in the various parts of their ranges by an abundance of geographically restricted and highly adapted species, thus indicating a lengthy evolution since their origin and prime dispersal.

Because relatively few bryophytes are endemics of restricted range and because so many identical or closely related species occupy widely disjunct areas, Herzog (8) postulated a slow rate of speciation, based on relatively few morphological characters by which variation can be expressed. Other factors seem to me more important: many mosses regularly reproduce asexually and have become widely distributed as unvarying clones in which genetic recombinations are impossible and recessive mutant characters do not find expression. Furthermore, many mosses are monoecious and through self-fertilization have become virtually homozygous and therefore unvarying. As small plants growing in the uniform conditions of microhabitats, bryophytes are not subject to the same environmental pressures which may force larger plants to adapt, move out, or die. For this reason, bryophytes may have survived quite catastrophic climatic or geological alterations in isolated niches, on small nunataks, for example, and their relict distributions in or near such areas may show phytogeographic links which would not otherwise be evident.

Our knowledge of fossil bryophytes, though meagre, supports the theory of an ancient, slowly evolving group. The two principal branches of the Bryophyta, the Musci and the Hepaticae, have been traced back to the Upper Carboniferous (Savicz-Ljubitskaja & Abramov, 12). Steere (18) reported that most Mesozoic and Cenozoic bryophytes known from North America belong to genera and perhaps even to species still growing on the continent. Most Quaternary fossil mosses could doubtless be identified as modern species if they were not so fragmentary and often poorly preserved.

In summary, it seems that the bryophytes are indeed ancient in origin but have evolved so slowly that specific disjuncts among the bryophytes may be comparable to generic disjuncts among the higher plants and are therefore equally useful to the phytogeographer.

Several familiar patterns of distribution demonstrate that mosses are similar in their distribution to higher plants and clearly reflect their floristic histories. A fair number of mosses are disjunct in eastern Africa and western South America, and a few of them occur in Madagascar and India as well. (I understand that the boa constrictor is found in Central America and Madagascar, a similar distribution difficult to explain by long-range, chance dispersal.) Irmscher (9) has cited many examples from all groups of plants of similar disjunction as evidence of continental drift, and I (5) have reviewed the problem, with evidence especially from bryophyte distributions. There are few mosses of widely disjunct bipolar distribution, recently noted by DuRietz (7), who was particularly concerned with lichens and higher plants of similar range. DuRietz suggested a polyphyletic origin for such disjunct species because he did not believe in the efficacy of long-range dispersal even to account for the jump across the lowlands at the Isthmus of Panama! Many mosses of eastern North America, particularly those of the ancient Southern Appalachian Mountains, are also found in eastern Asia. Their distributions are paralleled by many flowering plants known by fossil evidence and modern disjunctions to be relics of a circumpolar flora of late Mesozoic and early Tertiary times. A fairly large group of Pacific Coast species extend along the Aleutian chain of islands to Japan; some, disjunct at the ends, could be remnants of the Arcto-tertiary forest, as *Sequoia* and *Metasequoia* surely are. A few mosses characteristic of the Atlantic Coastal Plain of eastern North America and also widely distributed in the uplands of tropical America occur as disjuncts in the more ancient uplands of the southeast. Similarly disjunct flowering plants are considered remnants of a Miocene tropical invasion which later retreated into the Coastal Plain as a result of continental uplift. A very few tropical mosses may owe their presence in the essentially temperate flora of north-central Florida to a tropical flora on "Orange Island" of Oligocene time. A number of species seem to be relics in unglaciated nunataks of various sizes. The widely scattered occurrence of *Bryoxiphium* suggests that it survived the Pleistocene in local nunataks (Steere, 17).

In Alaska and the Yukon, a number of very rare mosses known other-wise from alpine or arctic-alpine ranges in Europe have been found, but only in unglaciated mountainous areas. The Driftless Area of the central United States includes a good number of boreal species far south of their present normal range; they are probably relics of some glacial advance or retreat that scoured the surrounding areas.

All these distributional phenomena are familiar to the phanerogamic botanist. It is not generally known, however, that bryophytes follow the same patterns of distribution and no doubt have had similar origins. It seems obvious that moss species occupy natural ranges just as the species of higher plants do.

A good share of the Canadian bryoflora is arctic or boreal and circumpolar in distribution. Very likely this large segment of the flora had a similarly broad distribution during the cool climates of the late Tertiary when land bridges apparently joined both Europe and Asia to North America at one time or another. Elements of this flora doubt-less survived the Pleistocene in various unglaciated areas, in part of the Arctic Archipelago, in the Brooks Range of Alaska, in some of the mountainous areas of the Canadian Northwest, and here and there along the Rocky Mountains, especially south of the Canadian border. Since the Pleistocene there has probably been some floristic exchange across the Bering Straits, but the bulk of the flora probably shifted back and forth with the successive advances and retreats of the Pleistocene ice. Since the temperate flora of southeastern Canada was surely derived from the south, and much of the boreal flora occupying the breadth of the country probably re-entered Canada from more southern latitudes, a review of the physiographic and phytogeographic history of the continent seems pertinent.

Since the appearance of angiosperms sometime in the Mesozoic, the world has suffered a number of vast geological transformations and climatic shifts that have profoundly affected plant distributions. The Cretaceous was a period of extensive continental erosion and sub-mergence throughout the world. By the end of the Cretaceous, the North American continent had been drastically altered in contour and relief. A shallow sea covered the Rocky Mountain trough from the Arctic Ocean to the Gulf of Mexico, and most of eastern North America had probably been reduced nearly to base level. The Mississippi Embayment extended from the present Gulf of Mexico to southern Illinois, and the Atlantic Coastal Plain was also submerged, as were most parts of Mexico, Central America, and the West Indies.

The elevation of the Rocky Mountains and associated movements of the earth's crust at the close of the Cretaceous resulted in the uplift of most of Mexico and parts of Central America and the Greater Antilles. East of the Rocky Mountains, the Central Plains were largely exposed, the Mississippi Embayment began to recede, and the inner Coastal Plain was exposed. The elevation of land surfaces ushering in the Tertiary initiated new cycles of erosion. In eastern North America, the Appalachian Highlands extending from southeastern Canada to central Alabama and the Ozark Plateau were greatly affected by peneplanation cycles culminating in the Miocene. Re-elevation, probably late in the Miocene, was followed in turn by continental erosion which was interrupted near the end of the Pliocene and has not yet been completed.

Mexico has been joined to the continent since the end of the Cretaceous, to Central America during most of the Tertiary, and to the Greater Antilles until upper Miocene or lower Pliocene times. During part of the time before the Pleistocene, the continent was also joined to Europe and to Asia, by more or less temporary land bridges. Such continuity of land surface and the mild and more uniform climates over the entire northern hemisphere during the Tertiary facilitated an exchange of floras between tropical and temperate parts of the Americas and also between the Old and New Worlds.

Four major areas in eastern North America have long been available as refugia for plants: the Southern Appalachian Mountains and adjacent highlands, the Interior Highlands (consisting of the Ozark and Ouachita Mountains), the Driftless Area in the plains of north-central United States, and the "Orange Island" area of north-peninsular Florida.

The Appalachian-Ozarkian Plateau has not been submerged since the Paleozoic and, except for its northern, glaciated portions (roughly south to the Ohio River), it has been continuously occupied by plants since long before the origin of angiosperms. The southern limit of Pleistocene glaciation and the northern extent of the earlier Mississippi Embayment make it convenient to divide this ancient plateau into two massive residual areas of which the eastern Appalachian area has been phytogeographically more significant because of its larger size and more favourable climates, past and present.

The outstanding phytogeographic feature of the Appalachian Highlands is the great mesophytic forest of ancient genera, many of which are known from fossil and modern distributions to have originated in the ancient Arcto-tertiary flora. The moderate climates of the late Mesozoic and early Tertiary favoured the development of a relatively homogeneous forest extending from Scandinavia and Spitsbergen across northern Eurasia to North America and Greenland and probably far southward at appropriate altitudes. The trend toward cooler and drier climates throughout the Tertiary resulted in a southward shift of the flora and a dissection of its range. In North America, the gradual desiccation of the continental interior as a result of orogeny in the west and the development of a new climatic regime along the Pacific Coast resulted in the elimination of most Tertiary genera in central and western parts of the continent. Relicts of the Arcto-tertiary flora still flourish in eastern America, eastern Asia, and, to some extent, in a few other places of known antiquity. In western North America a good number of Arcto-tertiary plants retreated to the mountains of Arizona and from there later invaded the Mexican and Guatemalan Highlands, thus accounting for a surprisingly close relationship of the Mexican and eastern North American floras.

The southern portion of the Appalachian Mountain system was most important as a refuge for Arcto-tertiary plants. According to Cain (2), the "virgin hardwood forest of the Great Smoky Mountains probably represents the greatest aggregation of Tertiary species now in existence in North America." Sharp (14) analyzed the modern distributions of genera represented in the Eocene Wilcox flora deposited along the margins of the Mississippi Embayment and found a strong relationship between the Wilcox and the modern floras of the Southern Appalachians, parts of Mexico and Guatemala, and eastern Asia. Most of the genera characteristic of the eastern North American deciduous forests, ranging from southeastern Canada to northern Florida and west to the prairies, have probably been derived from the Southern Appalachian refuge. During the Pleistocene, some Tertiary species may have moved to the more genial climates of the southern Coastal Plain, but, as Cain (3) pointed out, it is unlikely that entire associations of Tertiary relics now found in certain protected coves in the Southern Appalachians should have returned *en masse* after a Pleistocene exodus.

Of course, not all the ancient genera represented in the fossil Wilcox flora or in the modern forests of eastern North America can be traced to a northern, Arcto-tertiary origin. An interesting group of plants now characteristic of the relatively young Atlantic and Gulf Coastal Plains, but rather sparsely represented by disjuncts in the more ancient uplands, apparently came from the tropics during the Tertiary and were widespread in the Appalachian and Ozarkian areas during the extensive peneplanation and the warm, moist climates of the Miocene. On re-elevation, probably near the end of the Miocene, the area was converted from a low swampy plain into a well-drained upland favouring a more temperate, mesophytic flora. Many of the tropical species were forced to find suitable habitats in the newly emergent Coastal Plains. In some cases, isolated communities were left behind in the uplands, particularly on the Cumberland Plateau and in the Southern Appalachian Mountains.

Because of drier climates during late Tertiary and also post-glacial times, the Interior Highlands were less important in sheltering Arcto-tertiary plants, but the mixed mesophytic forest so well represented in the southern portion of the Appalachian Highlands is poorly represented there by relic communities, and a few endemics and disjuncts relate the flora to the Appalachian and eastern Asiatic floras (Braun, 1). A number of typical Coastal Plain species of tropical distribution or relationship have been found there as disjuncts giving evidence of a Miocene invasion from the American tropics (Steyermark, 20). As shown by considerable floristic affinity to the Edwards Plateau of Texas and the San Carlos Mountains of northeastern Mexico, the Ozark Highlands were no doubt important in an eastward extension of the prairie and a limited invasion of xerophytes from the arid Southwest during various post-glacial xerothermic periods.

The Driftless Area, a forested region surrounded by prairie and lying at the adjacent corners of Minnesota, Wisconsin, Illinois, and Iowa, has also been exposed since the Paleozoic and was never covered by the Pleistocene glaciers which at one time or another scoured all the surrounding area. Its type of vegetation, as well as a few endemic species, suggests a possible role as a plant refuge during the Pleistocene and later, during periods of prairie expansion.

There is some evidence that a part of north-central Florida may have had some significance as a plant refuge during part of the Tertiary. This area emerged as "Orange Island" during the Oligocene and was joined to the mainland by the close of the Miocene. The essentially temperate flora of the area includes a number of ferns of tropical distribution or affinity, many of them not found in the more tropical latitudes of southern Florida (St. John, 16); a few bryophytes are similarly restricted (Schornherst, 13). Woodson (21) showed that *Asclepias tuberosa* consists of three subspecies centered around Orange Island, the Southern Appalachians, and the Ozarks, and Camp (4) suggested the migration of certain South American species of *Gaylussacia* into eastern North America by way of the Antilles and Orange Island. Although Orange Island was probably useful in the northward migration of tropical species during the Tertiary, it is doubtful whether it was important in the survival of any species of modern Canadian distribution.

The actual importance of the major refugia during the vicissitudes of the Pleistocene is subject to question. There is no general agreement on the influence of the Pleistocene glaciers on continental climates or even on the distribution of plants quite near the southern limits of ice. For example, Deevey (6) reasoned that pollen profiles from the Pleistocene of the Gulf region and the presence of northern disjuncts in the Deep South today indicate that glacial chilling in the southeastern states must have been fairly extensive and that warmth-loving species, including many or perhaps most of the "Miocene relicts" survived in peninsular Florida and Mexico and have since returned to their present positions (that is, in the Coastal Plains and disjunctively in a few upland localities). Braun (1), on the other hand, said that both fossil and vegetational evidence indicate that the deciduous forest was displaced only in a band of varying width along the ice front, thus continuing the pattern of distribution which had been attained by the close of the Tertiary. It is certain, however, that many northern species did range as far south as the Gulf of Mexico during the Pleistocene and perhaps equally certain that many Tertiary species remained in the Southern Appalachian Mountains throughout the Pleistocene (Cain, 3). It has been suggested that glacial meltwater may have lowered the temperature of the ground water along river courses sufficiently to account for the migration of northern species far southward along the Mississippi River system, although species of the well-drained uplands may not have been greatly affected (Potzger & Friesner, 11).

The grandeur of the past may have aroused great expectations which can scarcely be fulfilled by our limited knowledge of moss distributions in Canada. It appears, however, that Canadian mosses, although broader in their distributions and showing very little endemism, occupy the same general ranges here as those outlined in Porsild's summary of geographic distributions of flowering plants and ferns (10). Collections have been too scattered and too sketchy to permit a detailed comparison, and any attempt to analyze the bryophytic composition of the various floristic regions or to work out phytogeographic affinities with precision seems premature and doomed to failure. The following observations are educated hunches, based on nearly twenty years of concentrated research on North American mosses, rather than on any exhaustive and authoritative analysis.

As one would expect from a history of severe and nearly complete glaciation in the not-too-distant past, the country is almost entirely occupied by aggressive, wide-ranging, ecologically undemanding species which show great variability, not because of unusual evolutionary potential, but because of seasonal response to environmental rigours and extremes. Most of the mosses now widespread in Canada probably occupied much the same wide ranges before glaciation, accompanied, however, by a large number of species which were less tolerant, less competitive, and less able to retreat to less suitable habitats southward. A good many of such species were preserved, however, in unglaciated parts of Alaska, the Yukon, and the northernmost islands of the Arctic Archipelago, as well as the Rocky Mountains and associated ranges south of the Canadian border. The vast Boreal Coniferous Forest occupies a completely glaciated area which scarcely offered any topographic impediment to a rapid and homogenous re-population mainly from the central plains of the United States, although there must have been some invasion of the area from northern and western residual areas as well. The bryophyte flora is depauperate and uniform throughout, clearly reflecting a uniformity of habitats as well as a re-population from an impoverished source. Most mosses of the boreal forest are circumpolar and of little phytogeographic interest.

The moss flora of the high arctic in many ways appears to be a mere attenuation of the flora of the boreal forest, but on closer inspection a surprising number of rare and interesting species may be discerned among those more characteristic of the boreal forest. This arctic element, mostly consisting of calciphiles, was recently publicized by Steere (19) in a paper particularly relating to the mosses of the ancient, unglaciated Brooks Range of Alaska. These species are mostly limited to the high arctic, but some few of them are represented in isolated stations far southward in the Rocky Mountains. Although many are found in the arctic of the Old World, a small number seem to be endemic to North America. The occurrence of the truly arctic element in the Yukon and in the Arctic Archipelago gives clear evidence of an old, northern flora residual in the arctic and re-distributed in post-Pleistocene times.

The survival of northern species on this continent was favoured by a north-south continuity of high mountains, whereas in Europe there is a considerable gap between the tundra vegetation of northern Scandinavia and that of the Alps. (It is erroneous and misleading to refer to the southward distribution of arctic plants in North America as arctic–alpine, as they are not comparable to the arctic–alpine disjunctions of Europe; I prefer to call them arctic-montane instead.) The Canadian

Rocky Mountains were heavily glaciated, but the American con-
tinuation, as well as the more western ranges of the Cordillera,
were not. Owing to dryness in the American Rockies now, and probably in the Pleistocene too, the arctic element is only poorly represented as far south as Colorado, although the presence of a few
rarities, such as *Oreas martiana* and *Voitia nivalis*, emphasize the
importance of the area as an arctic shelter. At least as far as mosses
are concerned, there is no distinctive flora of the Canadian Rocky
Mountains. It is rather a fairly rich assemblage of widespread calciphiles derived in post-Pleistocene times from the American Rockies
and the unglaciated mountains of Alaska and Yukon. Although it is
generally assumed, on the basis of logic rather than on the evidence
of distribution, that the Cordillera extending in a nearly unbroken
chain from the arctic to the antarctic has provided a broad highway
for easy plant migration north and south, the arctic and subarctic,
bryophytic flora is only meagerly represented as far south as Colorado,
and the Rocky Mountain and the Mexican floras are not even related.
Migration from South America is similarly limited. Only a few High
Andean species occur at the highest altitudes of central Mexico, and
none of them has penetrated the American or Canadian floras. There
are a very few bipolar species of mosses, occurring in some instances in
widely separated intermediate stations, but these are too widely
distributed in the northern hemisphere to be of any real phytogeographic interest and too few to be clearly referred to a history of
Cordilleran dispersal.

The flora of the Pacific Coast is the richest and most varied in
Canada. It includes a number of endemic species and even genera
in its total range which extends from northern California to southeastern Alaska and across the North Pacific in the Aleutian Islands. The
flora shows a strong relationship with that of Japan, and many of the
species appear to be Japanese-American disjuncts, but collections in
the Aleutians are too incomplete to show whether the ranges are
really discontinuous or not. The flora may have been derived in part
from the Arcto-Tertiary flora which virtually disappeared farther to
the south perhaps because of a change of climatic regime resulting in
summer dormancy and winter growth, but the virtual absence of the
eastern American species, disjunct in eastern Asia and so obviously
Arcto-Tertiary in origin, makes it more logical to seek some other,
more recent floristic exchange with Japan.

The Canadian prairie has a very limited flora of widespread and
weedy species. It may be rich in ephemerals of considerable interest,

as the American prairies are, but this one interesting element of the flora has been almost completely neglected.

The deciduous forest of the Appalachian Highlands is represented by a mere fringe in southeastern Canada, especially in southern Ontario and Quebec. The mosses which reach their northern limits here are all widespread, mostly filling the entire range of the deciduous forest from southeastern Canada to northern Florida and west to the prairies. Some are American endemics, but the majority also occur in Europe, Asia, or both. Those of European occurrence may have occupied North America at some pre-glacial time when land connections existed between Europe and North America. Those of Asiatic disjunction very likely remain from the ancient Arcto-tertiary forest. Both groups were, of course, derived secondarily from the Appalachian Highlands following glaciation.

The temperate flora of the Maritimes is similar to that of New England and the Alleghany Mountain system. Although there is some possibility of the eastern montane species surviving glaciation in small local nunataks, as in the Gaspé for example, there is no real evidence among the bryophytes, so far as I know. Most of the flora could easily have been derived from the mountains of the eastern United States where the flora is essentially similar at higher altitudes as far south as North Carolina.

A small but interesting group of northern and Cordilleran disjuncts occur around the shores of Lake Superior and also in calcareous areas fringing the other Great Lakes, the St. Lawrence Valley, and the Gaspé. Most of the calciphiles grow in wet habitats, often in unstable situations, such as seepage areas at lake shores. I would guess that they are relics of glacial retreat persisting where they do because the habitats are right and there is no ecological pressure to move on. Those of the Lake Superior region, such as *Cnestrum schisti*, *Mielichhoferia mielichhoferiana*, and *Timmia austriaca*, may also be relics of a glacial retreat, stopping there for purely edaphic reasons, but because of the rugged nature of the terrain, they may have persisted there in small niches unaffected by glaciation.

I have tried to show that moss distributions in Canada, though somewhat more diffuse than those of higher plants, reflect a similar history of migration. Because of a slow rate of evolution resulting in wide specific distributions and broad specific disjunctions, mosses in some cases show phytogeographic relationships not readily apparent from a study of phanerogams, such as the relationship of the Pacific Coast flora to Japan.

REFERENCES

1. BRAUN, E. L.   1950.   Deciduous Forests of Eastern North America. Blakiston
   Co., Philadelphia. 596 pp.
2. CAIN, S. A.   1939.   The climax and its complexities. Am. Midl. Nat. *21*:
   146–181.
3. ⸺ 1943.   The Tertiary character of the cove hardwood forest of the Great
   Smoky Mountains National Park. Bull. Torrey Botan. Club *70*: 213–235.
4. CAMP, W. H.   1941.   Studies in Ericales: A review of the North American
   Gaylussaciae; with remarks on the origin and migrations of the group.
   Bull. Torrey Botan. Club *68*: 531–555.
5. CRUM, H.   1956.   Notes on *Hypnodon*, a genus of Orthotrichaceae new to
   North America. Bryologist *59*: 26–34.
6. DEEVEY, E. S., JR.   1949.   Biogeography of the Pleistocene. Bull. Geol. Soc.
   Am. *60*: 1316–1416.
7. DuRIETZ, G. E.   1940.   Problems of bipolar plant distribution. Acta Phyto-
   geogr. Suec. *13*: 215–282.
8. HERZOG, T.   1926.   Geographie der Moose. Gustav Fischer, Jena. 439 pp.
9. IRMSCHER, E.   1929.   Pflanzenverbreitung und Entwicklung der Kontinente.
   II. Weitere Beiträge zur genetischen Pflanzengeographie unter besonderer
   Berücksichtigung der Laubmoose. Mitt. Inst. allg. Bot. Hamburg *8*:
   169–347.
10. PORSILD, A. E.   1958.   Geographical distribution of some elements in the
    flora of Canada. Geograph. Bull. *11*: 57–77.
11. POTZGER, J. E., and R. C. FRIESNER.   1939.   Plant migration in the southern
    limits of Wisconsin glaciation in Indiana. Am. Midl. Nat. *22*: 351–368.
12. SAVICZ-LJUBITSKAJA, L. I., and I. I. ABRAMOV.   1958.   Geological annals of
    Bryophyta. Botan. Zhur. *43*: 1409–1417 (in Russian).
13. SCHORNHERST, R. O.   1943.   Phytogeographic studies of the mosses of
    northern Florida. Am. Midl. Nat. *29*: 509–532.
14. SHARP, A. J.   1951.   The relation of the Eocene Wilcox flora to some modern
    floras. Evolution *5*: 1–5.
15. SKOTTSBERG, C.   1956.   Derivation of flora and fauna of Juan Fernandez and
    Easter Island. *1*(5): 193–438. *In* The Natural History of Juan Fernandez
    and Easter Island. Almquist & Wiksell, Uppsala. 3 vols., 2086 pp.
16. ST. JOHN, E. P.   1936.   Rare ferns of central Florida. Am. Fern Jour. *26*:
    41–50.
17. STEERE, W. C.   1937.   *Bryoxiphium norvegicum*, the sword moss, as a
    preglacial and interglacial relic. Ecology *18*: 346–358.
18. ⸺ 1946.   Cenozoic and Mesozoic bryophytes of North America. Am. Midl.
    Nat. *36*(2): 298–324.
19. ⸺ 1953.   On the geographical distribution of arctic bryophytes. *In* I. L.
    Wiggins, ed., Current Biological Research in the Alaskan Arctic. Stanford
    Univ. Publ. Biol. Sci. *11*: 30–47.
20. STEYERMARK, J. A.   1950.   Flora of Guatemala. Ecology *31*: 368–372.
21. WOODSON, R. E., JR.   1947.   Notes on the "historical factor" in plant
    geography. Contr. Gray Herb. *165*: 12–25.
22. WULFF, E. V.   1950.   An Introduction to Historical Plant Geography.
    Chronica Botanica Co., Waltham, Mass. 223 pp.
23. ZIMMERMAN, E. C.   1948.   Insects of Hawaii. *1*: 1–206.

THEODORE MOSQUIN

Reproductive Specialization as a Factor in the Evolution of the Canadian Flora

IT IS NOW GENERALLY RECOGNIZED that climate has been the major factor influencing the patterns of higher plant evolution. According to Axelrod (1, 2), Corner (12, 13), Richards (46), Delevoryas (18), and many others, most higher plant families very probably originated in the widespread tropical climates during Mesozoic time. Then, in the great expansion of temperate climates that followed the Mesozoic, the derivatives of these early tropical floras gradually invaded and became diversified in the expanding colder climates where numerous specialized evolutionary lines were produced. The Canadian flora represents, for the most part, end-products of this evolution from the tropics. The hereditary changes associated with the evolution of plants especially qualified for the colonization of the regions with colder climates are only now beginning to be understood. This increased understanding is due mainly to the recent application of the principles of genetics and cytogenetics to solutions of problems associated with the evolution of natural populations. Many writers have attempted to identify the particular attributes which impart superior adaptive properties in the colder climates. In this paper I shall examine a new hypothesis, namely, that reproductive specializations which promote genetic uniformity of populations have played the dominant role in the adaptation and evolution of our flora from plants of the lower latitudes.

Evolutionary specializations which play a role in the progressive adaptation of plants to a new environment are of two very different types. The first includes modifications of vegetative morphology, anatomy, and physiological and ecological response while the second concerns changes in reproductive biology. The structure and the functions of a plant determine adaptation and survival only in the present generation, but reproductive biology controls the features that this generation will pass on to succeeding generations. The key role of reproductive specializations in evolution lies in their ability to restrict or to promote genetic variability by an assortment of devices, and thereby to control the amount of morphological and physiological variability upon which natural selection can operate.

Stebbins (57, 58, 59), Baker (5), Corner (12, 13), Gustafsson (24), and many others have noted that reproductive systems of plants are closely linked with the kinds of environment to which their populations are adapted. Thus vegetative reproduction, self-pollination, and polyploidy are common in cold climates, self-pollination in weedy habitats, self-incompatibility in temperate regions, wind pollination in the temperate forests, and so on. Such correlations imply clear-cut cause and effect relationships between reproductive systems and environment. However, although a particular reproductive method may be relatively common in a certain region or zone, other equally successful types may also be present. Certain genetic factors of which reproductive systems are comprised may have a far greater effect on variability than others, and also different combinations of genetic factors can produce the same effect on variability. If we wish to discover whether or not different floristic or ecological zones have significantly different levels of genetic variability and also to understand how this variability is controlled, then reproductive factors in each species of a region or zone must first be identified and evaluated using established genetic principles. Then, multiple correlations between genetic and environmental factors must be made.

This paper is divided into two parts. The first part deals with the factors which enter into the construction of reproductive methods of higher plants, examines the question of what constitutes a reproductively specialized genetic system, and concludes with a general hypothesis relating to the Canadian flora. The second part is a detailed breakdown of our flora by ecological zones and taxonomic groups and provides tests for the hypothesis.

When we speak of reproductive specializations, we imply that they have been derived from an ancestral system. What then, constitutes a reproductively ancestral system? Fossils have been too few and fragmentary to solve this problem but they are not required for a satisfactory solution because many examples of definitely determined evolutionary sequences in factors influencing reproductive systems are known from living plants. The directions of these sequences and whether they are reversible have been experimentally demonstrated and can be inferred from many dozens of genera (Stebbins, 57; Darlington, 15, 16). Furthermore, reproductively specialized genetic systems *must* be defined in terms of genetic and cytological principles because the reproductive biology of fossil plants cannot be studied.

In defining a reproductively ancestral genetic system, Darlington (16, pp. 39–41) has introduced the useful concept of an "ideal ancestor." An ideal ancestor is one which has the inherent capacity to give rise to all presently known genetic systems and not become extinct itself. Ideal ancestors would have a large measure of evolutionary flexibility and would have or could have a free exchange of genes. They would be diploid, often with a genetic incompatibility system favouring cross-pollination, meiosis would be regular with chiasmata distributed throughout the chromosomes, and all individuals would be moderately heterozygous with no two individuals exactly alike. Such an ancestral system would likely be comprised of hermaphrodites, i.e., of plants having perfect flowers (Crowe, 14). It would extend back in time beyond the beginnings of the Angiosperms (see Whitehouse, 64) and would be common in most groups today. Highly specialized genetic or reproductive systems are very unlikely to be ancestral to other kinds of genetic systems.

The two principal effects of reproductive specialization are shown on the left and on the right sides of Fig. 1. Starting from the ideal ancestor in the centre, toward the left we have those reproductive specializations which serve to increase the amount of genetic uniformity in populations. Toward the right we have the kinds of trends which, if present, serve to promote variability. The heavy arrows indicate well-documented lines of evolutionary specialization; the thin arrows indicate occasional reversibility. I shall deal briefly with each of these avenues and then attempt to show how each avenue has influenced the reproductive systems of our species and the evolution of our flora. The factors leading to genetic uniformity will be considered first.

Apomixis. The genetic effect of apomixis is the production of clones or pure lines. Apomicts normally originate from outcrossers (Stebbins, 57) and many intermediate stages between sexuality and obligate apomixis exist (Gustafsson, 24). The more nearly obligate the apomixis

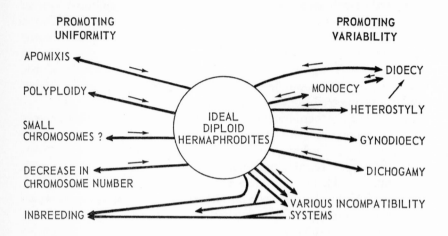

PROMOTING
UNIFORMITY

PROMOTING
VARIABILITY

APOMIXIS

POLYPLOIDY

SMALL
CHROMOSOMES ?

DECREASE IN
CHROMOSOME NUMBER

INBREEDING

IDEAL
DIPLOID
HERMAPHRODITES

DIOECY

MONOECY

HETEROSTYLY

GYNODIOECY

DICHOGAMY

VARIOUS INCOMPATIBILITY
SYSTEMS

REPRODUCTIVE FACTORS AFFECTING POPULATION VARIABILITY

Figure 1

the more would the clones be protected from genetic recombination.

Polyploidy. The effect of polyploidy on the genetic system is to put a strong damper on the evolutionary process. Stebbins (57) has noted that although polyploids may produce some new variation on an old theme, they never seem to produce any major new departures. This conservative characteristic of polyploids is in direct contrast to the dynamic evolutionary potential of diploids, as is clear from studies of numerous genera like *Crepis* (Babcock, 3), *Clarkia* (Lewis, 35), and many others.

An important mechanism responsible for imposing evolutionary limitations on polyploids has only recently been identified. It is a genic factor which prevents the formation of multivalent associations or their equivalents and thereby prevents the attainment of homozygosity of the many allelic genes on homologous chromosome segments. In such polyploids, bivalent formation is the rule. Genic control has been described recently from the hexaploid wheats (Riley, 47, 48; Riley and Kempanna, 49; Riley and Chapman, 50; Kimber and Riley, 31) and may also occur in polyploid *Gossypium* (Kimber, 30). That such genic control is probably very widespread among polyploids is suggested by the fact that many even very high polyploids show only bivalent formation. Segmental allopolyploids, which may be very variable because of intergenomic exchange also appear to be unable to produce radically new departures. Polyploidy is considered to represent an efficient buffering system, resisting the effects of natural selection on particular alleles and promoting as well as preserving phenotypic uniformity in populations. Polyploidy in general, therefore, acts like a sponge, absorbing mutations but rarely expressing them. The higher the level of polyploidy, the more conservative and buffered the reproductive system.

Small chromosomes. Smaller chromosomes are known to have fewer chiasmata and are thought to have fewer genetic crossovers (Swanson, 61) and therefore, reduced recombination. Plants with small chromosomes would thus tend to have more uniform genotypes.

Decrease in chromosome number. This device for increasing population uniformity applies mainly to certain genera of arid regions (see Stebbins, 57). It has little application to our flora and I shall not consider it further.

Inbreeding. Another of the great avenues of reproductive specialization in higher plants is that from outbreeding toward progressively greater inbreeding. Evidence for this far-reaching and important generalization comes from a variety of observations. These are: (1) Self-pollination is very strongly correlated with morphologically, ecologically, and cytologically specialized plants. For example, selfing occurs in annuals, at the ends of descending aneuploid series as in *Crepis* (Babcock, 3), in restrictive habitats, and among weedy floras. (2) The great majority of our cultivated plants are self-fertilized and many have originated from known outcrossing relatives in historical times (Darlington, 16). (3) Automatic selfers are usually closely related to certain outcrossing species and are presumably derived directly from them, while outcrossing species frequently bridge the gaps between genera. (4) Most inbreeders contain flower features which are rudiments of outbreeding ancestry: for example, the small but colourful corollas of selfing *Trifolium* species and the lodicules of autogamous grasses (Stebbins, 59).

Evidence of a more general nature is also available. Stebbins (59), after reviewing breeding systems in the tribe Cichorieae of the Compositae concluded that, throughout that large group of plants, there was overwhelming evidence that inbreeders evolved from outcrossers and not vice versa. Numerous other workers (Chambers, 11; Raven, 44; Moore and Lewis, 38) have come to the same conclusion with respect to other groups. Selfers, therefore, frequently arise from outcrossers, but the reverse rarely, if ever occurs. The genetic consequences of pronounced inbreeding on the reproductive system is usually to drastically reduce heterozygosity and to increase as well as to promote homozygosity.

Let us now give attention to reproductive devices that promote variability. Experimental evidence for the lines of specialization as noted on the right side of Fig. 1 is not as conclusive as for specializations promoting uniformity but what evidence is available suggests that the arrows are substantially correct, at least for many groups that have been studied (Crowe, 14).

Monoecy and dioecy. Monoecy occurs when stamens and pistils are on different flowers of the same plant; dioecy occurs when male and female flowers are on separate plants. Many species have genetic systems which combine various degrees of hermaphroditism, monoecy, and dioecy. Lewis (33) and Crowe (14), who studied the morphological and experimental evidence for evolutionary sequences among outbreeding plants, concluded that dioecious plants had evolved principally from monoecious ones and Darlington (15) has suggested that there are evolutionary sequences even in dioecy. It is clear that the avenue of reproductive specialization toward dioecy will result in progressively greater outcrossing and more population variability. Baker (5) considered dioecy to be the most drastic form of outcrossing.

Heterostyly. Most heterostyled species have two types of flowers: some plants of the population have flowers with long styles and short stamens and the rest have flowers with short styles and long stamens. Because self-incompatibility alleles are normally found in heterostyled plants, such plants cannot usually be self-fertilized, and seed set generally occurs only when the two flower types are intercrossed. There is no doubt that heterostyly is a derived and specialized form of outcrossing (Crowe 13) and that it tends to increase the amount of variability.

Gynodioecy. Gynodioecy is a condition where some plants of the species are female, others are hermaphrodite. Some degree of outcrossing is therefore necessary for seed set, at least in the females.

Dichogamy. Dichogamy is the differential timing of stigma receptiveness and anther maturation. It is probably quite common but has scarcely been studied in our flora. It is apparent that the greater the degree of dichogamy, the more will outcrossing be favoured.

Incompatibility systems. The most common mechanism favouring outcrossing is that of incompatibility genes (East, 22; Fryxell, 23; Crowe, 14). Lewis (34), Crowe (14), Bateman (6), and others have classified the various kinds of incompatibility systems and have shown that plants with some incompatibility systems would be more stringent outcrossers than those with other kinds of systems. Crowe (14) has also shown that all types of incompatibility systems appear to be phylogenetically related and that each of them can break down, giving rise to inbreeding as is shown in Fig. 1.

Summarizing, we can say that the factors listed on the right of Fig. 1, while they might increase the relative amount of variability, do not have a genetic effect which is radically different from that of the ideal diploid hermaphrodites. This is in sharp contrast to the factors on the left, some of which, when present even alone, have a profound impact on the genetic system since the evolutionary result is relative uniformity of populations and a decrease in evolutionary potential.

In addition to the reproductive factors listed in Fig. 1, there are two vegetative factors which affect the level of variability of genetic systems. These are long life cycles, and seed dispersal mechanisms. Long life cycles permit direct crossing between parents and offspring and increase inbreeding. Good seed dispersal mechanisms have the opposite effect. If seeds are widely scattered, the chances of close relative mating are reduced and outcrossing would be promoted.

Environmental factors are of primary importance in determining the kind and degrees of reproductive specialization since, after all, it is the environment which shapes reproductive systems through the process of natural selection. Ecological conditions and climatic factors, particularly if they act over appreciable periods of geological time, are especially important in this regard. Pollen transport agents are also very important and will be briefly considered in the Discussion. In dealing with the effects of ecological and climatic factors on the evolution of our flora we come to the central hypothesis of this paper, namely, that in order to colonize and grow in ever more northern climatic regions as well as in environments maintained by man, plants must evolve the kinds of reproductive systems which promote and preserve a high degree of genotypic uniformity in populations. Thus, species having diverse evolutionary lineages but at present occupying similar ecological conditions or climatic zones would be expected to have a comparable capacity to express genetic variability. Whatever the kinds and proportions of reproductive components in a genetic system of a particular species, the effect on the level of population variability will be very similar. In some ecological or climatic zones, many species will have reproductive systems which are comprised of contradictory genetic components. I feel that evidence is available to strongly suggest that certain of these apparently contradictory components will, on analysis, prove to be largely vestigial and therefore non-adaptive. Elaboration, amplification, and documentation of these statements together with a number of additional corollaries will now be considered.

The gradual increase from south to north in reproductive systems favouring genetic uniformity becomes apparent when we consider each of the factors listed on Fig. 1. Thus apomixis, in many of its forms, is well known from the arctic (Gustafsson, 24). Polyploidy increases from about 30 per cent in the tropics to between 80 and 90 per cent in some areas of the arctic (Löve and Löve, 36; Reese, 45; Johnson and Packer, 29). Smaller chromosomes are also very common, especially in some of the larger groups like *Salix* (Westergaard, 63), *Juncus* (Snogerup, 54), and the Cyperaceae (Wahl, 62; Moore and Calder, 39; Hicks, 27). Inbreeding, mostly by self-pollination, becomes progressively more common toward the arctic although it also may be widespread in the tropics (Corner, 12). In the same way as factors promoting uniformity of populations increase with latitude, factors promoting variability decrease. Thus monoecy and dioecy are found in numerous genera of temperate regions (Yampolsky and Yampolsky, 65) but the percentage of genera with these two outcrossing devices decreases sharply with latitude. Heterostyly is relatively common in the middle latitudes but is rare or not known in the arctic. Gynodioecy is common in some groups in the tropics and warm temperate regions but rare in our flora. Virtually nothing is known of the relation of dichogamy to latitude. Self-incompatibility associated with outcrossing appears to be the norm in temperate regions (Lewis, 34; Crowe, 14). The repeated breakdown of various kinds of incompatibility systems of temperate plants appears to have been of major importance in permitting the successful invasion of many families into the ever higher latitudes.

Similar generalizations concerning increases in the frequencies of factors promoting genetic constancy can be made about our weedy flora.

ECOLOGICAL ZONES

Turning now to the details of the Canadian Flora, the major phytogeographic zones will be considered first, then some common taxonomic groups. Only angiosperms and gymnosperms, both introduced and native, are included in the study. Six regional floras, representative of the major floristic zones, have been selected for comparison, and the location of each is shown in Fig. 2. The most northern sample is from what can be called the "botanical north pole" of North America, located

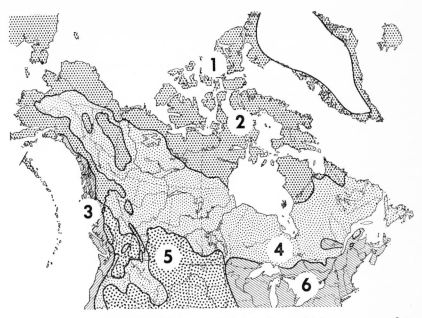

FIGURE 2. The geographical location of the six floras which are compared in Figure 3.

on Ellef Ringnes Island, a region having one of the most severe polar climates of this continent. According to Savile (52) the region includes only 49 species. The second flora is that of the Arctic Archipelago by Porsild (43). The third is that of the Queen Charlotte Islands, now in preparation by Calder and Taylor (10). The fourth is the flora of the boreal forest as exemplified by plants growing in the Great Clay Belt of north-central Ontario based on the work of Baldwin (4). The fifth flora is that of the prairies based on the work of Budd (9), although his flora is incomplete, particularly for *Carex* and *Salix*, and the sixth flora is that of southern Ontario based on the records of Soper (55).

Estimates of the amount and the kind of genetic variability in the plants of a floristic or ecological zone must, at present, be based on subjective judgments of each species in the zone. When making estimates we must weigh the relative importance of the various factors which enter into the construction of the genetic system. For example, apomixis promotes uniformity but may occur with dioecy which promotes variability (as in *Antennaria*). Similarly, polyploid or apomictic plants may have the large flowers of typical outcrossers (as in *Papaver* and *Potentilla* respectively). At the same time, only *one* of the reproductive traits listed in Fig. 1 will often have a profoundly greater impact on population variability than will all other traits combined. For example, the presence of nearly obligate apomixis, very strong inbreeding, or a high level of polyploidy are alone usually decisive in ensuring a high degree of genotypic uniformity in populations. Based on these considerations I have made estimates of the relative amount of variability in every species of each of these six floras and the results are presented in the form of histograms shown in Fig. 3. Each histogram has eight classes, A to H, and each species in these floras has

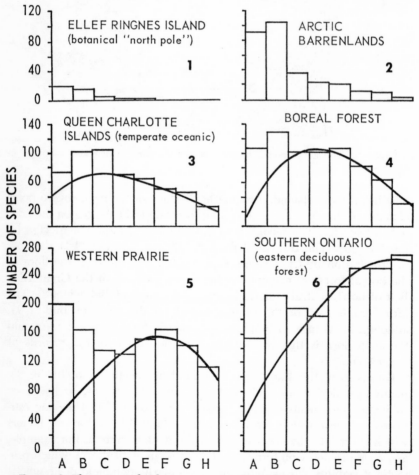

FIGURE 3. The estimated relative amounts of population variability in species of six floralistic regions of Canada.

been assigned to one of the eight classes. Class A of this arbitrary range includes the kinds of species which are either very highly polyploid (some *Saxifraga* species), strongly apomictic (for example, some species of *Antennaria, Arnica, Potentilla, Taraxacum*, and of the Gramineae), or strongly inbred (for example *Koenigia islandica, Corydalis sempervirens*, and autogamous grasses), whereas Class H includes species normally diploid, sexual, and at the same time having the kinds of floral features that very strongly favour cross-pollination (for example *Epilobium angustifolium* and *Dryas integrifolia*). No firm rules were followed when assigning any species to the intermediate classes. For example, *Salix* species, which are dioecious (a condition promoting variability) and also perennial, have small chromosomes, and may be polyploid (conditions all promoting uniformity), were assigned to classes C to G depending on chromosome number if known. Monoecious *Carex* species were assigned to the area between B and E since small chromosomes, polyploidy and perennity are characteristic of the species and inbreeding is suspected (see later discussion). Outcrossing grasses were scored between D and H, again depending on the degree of perennity and on the level of ploidy. Submerged aquatics presented the most difficult problems and in assigning some species, a great deal of subjective judgment was exercised.

Each of the histograms in Fig. 3 includes all the species in the region, whether native or weedy. While scoring the species I found that most introduced weeds as well as those native species behaving as weeds nearly always fell into Classes A to C. A curve has been drawn in the middle and lower histograms in order to provide a rough estimate of the proportions of weedy (above the curve) to non-weedy (below the curve) species in each of these four floras. Curves were not drawn in the top histograms since introduced weeds are absent from the arctic regions. Taken together, the six histograms demonstrate that both arctic plants and temperate weeds have strikingly parallel genetic systems—both have a preponderance of reproductive devices promoting uniformity. The histograms also clearly establish that the amount of genetic variability in the non-weedy native floras decreases sharply as one goes from temperate to arctic environments.

REPRODUCTIVE PATTERNS IN SOME MAJOR GROUPS

The Cruciferae, a family whose reproductive biology is fairly well known, contains some 350 genera and 2,500 species of temperate and cold regions (Lawrence, 32). Bateman (7) reviewed the breeding systems of 182 species of 69 genera and 11 tribes. He showed that self-incompatibility was a very important outbreeding mechanism operating throughout the family. Also, most of the genera have produced self-compatible and even automatically self-pollinated derivatives. Large flowers and conspicuous inflorescences were associated with self-incompatibility. Medium-sized flowers were often self-compatible but plants with small flowers were usually automatically self-pollinated. Meiotic and mitotic chromosome studies are at present being made on numerous Canadian Cruciferae by Mulligan so that the distribution of polyploidy and apomixis in Canadian species can be correlated with Bateman's conclusions concerning incompatibility systems.

The genus *Erysimum* of the Cruciferae has a number of strongly scented, large-flowered, self-incompatible species native to the western United States and adjacent Canada. However, one species, *Erysimum inconspicuum*, occurring from the Gaspé to the Yukon and south to New Mexico, has much smaller non-scented flowers. Its populations are apomictic; various chromosome numbers and also disturbed meiosis are the norm. The large-flowered, presumably outcrossed species, *E. pallasii* of the arctic, also has disturbed meiosis and is probably apomictic.

The genus *Lesquerella* of the Cruciferae has its greatest diversity in the western United States and adjacent Canada where many large- and medium-flowered, apparently self-incompatible species have arisen, mostly by aneuploidy at the diploid level. Only one species, *Lesquerella arctica* occurs in the arctic and it is self-pollinated. It also has the highest known chromosome numbers of the genus (Mulligan, unpublished) and, therefore, represents a highly buffered genetic system. The remaining arctic genera *Cochlearia, Eutrema, Cardamine, Draba, Halimolobos, Braya, Parrya, Arabis,* and *Descurainia* are either polyploid or self-pollinated or both, and some may yet prove to be apomictic. Mulligan (41) has also shown that the great majority of crucifers in our weedy habitats are self-pollinated; or, if they are perennial, self-incompatible, and actively insect-visited like *Cardaria,* they are repeatedly introduced into fields by man.

The family Leguminosae is the third largest of higher plants with some 550 genera and 12,000 species (Lawrence, 32). Most legumes are diploid and have showy flowers specialized for insect pollination. In the tropics the Leguminosae attains its greatest diversity, with hundreds of endemic genera, mostly shrubs and trees often actively visited by both insects and birds (Corner, 12). In temperate regions, legumes are either cross-fertilized by insects or are highly inbred by selfing. If they are selfers, then they often tend to behave like weeds. When weedy legumes are self-incompatible (and often actively visited by insects) then they are perennial or they have the capacity to spread vegetatively as for example *Ulex europaeus, Cytisus scoparius, Trifolium pratense, T. repens, T. hybridum*, and *Lotus corniculatus* (see Fryxell, 23, for references). In southern Canada, most of the genera are showy flowered, and many species among them are known to be cross-fertilized, for example, *Hedysarum, Astragalus*, and *Lupinus* (Fryxell, 23). Self-compatibility is, however, known in *Lupinus, Lathyrus, Vicia*, and *Trifolium* and is scattered throughout the temperate genera (Fryxell, 23). Only two genera of this family are relatively successful in the arctic, namely, the perennials *Oxytropis* and *Astragalus*. Observations of flowers and of seed set on herbarium specimens of these two genera from arctic regions indicate that they are probably automatically self-pollinated. In field observations on Melville Island, N.W.T., at 75°N, I found *Oxytropis arctica* (large showy flowers) to be scentless and very rarely visited by bumble bees but *Astragalus alpinus* (medium showy flowers) to be very strongly scented and actively visited by bumble bees. However, it is not clear whether the bees are essential for fertilization and seed set.

The family Scrophulariaceae is comparable to the legumes in that most of its members of low and middle latitudes are diploid and have flowers especially adapted for insect or bird pollination. According to the list made by Fryxell (23), practically all Scrophulariaceae are self-incompatible. The only genera invading northern polar climates are *Pedicularis, Euphrasia*, and *Castilleja* all of which, on the basis of herbarium observations, I consider to be strongly self-pollinated despite the presence in the arctic of many active flower-visiting insects (see Downes 19, 20, 21, for references). In my field observations on Melville Island I failed to see a single bumble bee on either *Pedicularis sudetica* or *P. arctica* the latter of which was very common throughout the region. Sprague (56) in a remarkable study of pollination patterns in the genus found on the basis of a number of lines of evidence that northern *Pedicularis* species may produce seed by autogamy, but that in temperate regions species of this genus normally depend on insects for seed set. Among the weedy Scrophulariceae of temperate regions, annuals like *Chaenorrhinum* and some *Veronica* species are selfers, but species like *Linaria vulgaris* and *L. dalmatica* are outcrossers, with extensive perennating systems.

The family Rosaceae extends from the tropics to the arctic but unlike the Leguminosae and the Scrophulariaceae, it has few self-pollinated species or races in our area. If we can use the summary by Fryxell (23) as a guide, virtually all members of this family are strongly self-incompatible and it is well known that genera like *Spiraea, Prunus, Amelanchier, Rosa* and others are very actively visited by many kinds of insects. According to McAlpine (37) active insect visiting is true even for the genus *Dryas* of the western mountains and high arctic. It would be interesting to know whether the more northern representatives of the sexual, presumably diploid populations of *Dryas* and *Sibbaldia* have lost the self-incompatibility characteristic of the family, and to study the seed set and the pollination biology of populations of these genera at the northern limits of their range. Although the evolution of self-pollinating races does not appear to be an important avenue open to the Rosaceae in our area, another avenue toward genotypic uniformity, namely, that of apomixis, is being actively explored. Apomixis has been superimposed upon sexual outcrossing systems in both *Potentilla* of the alpine and arctic regions and in *Rubus* and *Crataegus* of temperate weedy habitats.

The Orchidaceae are of special interest because our native species are neither weeds nor do they grow in the arctic. Bingham (8) has shown that the half-dozen orchid genera of the boreal forests require insects for seed set although whether or not any species is self-compatible is apparently not known. Presumably, outcrossing or at least self-pollination by insects is necessary for seed set. The chromosome numbers of northern orchids are quite high and presumably genetic variability is buffered to some extent. Raup (43) and Savile and Calder (personal communication) have observed numerous mosquitoes with orchid pollinia attached to their eyes and presumably mosquitoes are effective pollinators.

Dozens of excellent examples of the close relationship between relatively uniform environments and constant genetic systems are also found in the Canadian Compositae and Gramineae and in many smaller groups.

The genera *Carex* and *Salix*, since they are rich in numbers of species, appear at first to be exceptions to the hypothesis that a great deal of genetic uniformity is at a selective advantage at higher latitudes. *Carex*, a protogynous wind-pollinated genus, is mostly monoecious or occasionally dioecious (Lawrence, 32). It has not been established by experiment whether any one of the 2,500 species of *Carex* can be self-pollinated. Most *Carex* species grow at the margins of bogs, in open areas of the arctic and often on open sites normally exposed to wind.

However, in most monoecious species the male flowers are normally located immediately above the female and drop large amounts of pollen on the latter. If monoecious *Carex* species are self-compatible and normally self-pollinated they would be strongly inbred. Clearly experimental studies of pollination biology in this large genus would be very useful. Plants of this genus have remarkably small chromosomes and presumably a reduced amount of crossing over and increased linkage. Davies (17) and others have shown that in numerous *Carex* species, most chromosomes are duplicated one or more times by aneuploidy. Therefore, in addition to the presumed inbreeding, *Carex* species might, like polyploids, possess highly buffered genetic systems because of extensive chromosomal duplications.

The genus *Salix* is dioecious and most species are actively visited by insects (Hjelmqvist, 28). Very small chromosomes are also a feature of this genus. Polyploidy is extremely common and without doubt serves as an efficient buffering system, thereby restricting genetic variability. It is possible that *Salix* might also represent a genus in which a great deal of inbreeding occurs by repeated close relative mating. Both *Carex* and *Salix* are perennial so that vegetative reproduction can also serve as a basis for uniform populations.

DISCUSSION

The broad pattern of reproductive specialization in the Canadian flora appears to be one in which both native plants as well as weeds have adopted a variety of devices and combinations of devices for achieving a large measure of population uniformity. Stebbins (59), in his review of evolutionary patterns in the tribe Cichorieae of the Compositae, showed that in that large group of plants at least three devices were present which reduced genetic recombination and thereby achieved population constancy. Those three were aneuploid decrease in chromosome number, apomixis, and self-pollination. However, only one device operated in any one species. It seems clear that a similar adaptive process has produced the south to north and the native to weedy adaptation patterns but that in northern and weedy floras more than one device for promoting genetic constancy has occurred in many species as the examples above indicate.

As mentioned earlier, many species growing in weedy and in boreal-arctic regions have some features promoting genetic constancy but at the same time possess other features which normally promote variability. The presence of these combinations of opposing reproductive factors in a plant may be explained by assuming that each of the factors has an adaptive function which contributes toward maintaining the required *balance* in variability of the genetic system and this is undoubtedly true in some groups. However, a much more likely explanation for the presence of the numerous opposing tendencies, at least in the higher latitude floras, is that most of the reproductive features which normally promote variability have only a limited or no adaptive function today. It appears reasonable to consider that much of the genetic variability in northern regions represents a lag behind the present adaptive requirements of the genetic system—requirements which are largely physiological and as yet undefined. A logical conclusion to this line of reasoning as it applies to northern floras is that even genetic variability itself may be largely a vestigial feature in the higher latitudes. The capacity to produce variability is certainly deep-seated genetically, and we would not expect this capacity to be easily lost or replaced. As examples of non-adaptive outcrossing features in arctic plants we might consider the specialized flowers of the Leguminosae and Scrophulariaceae. These flowers are not evidence of specialized pollinator relationships having adaptive value but rather of outcrossing in the ancestry because, judging from herbarium specimens and field observations (Savile, 51, pp. 987–88), most species of these two families in the higher latitudes must be self-pollinated. Likewise the colourful and conspicuous flowers of arctic representatives of genera like *Arnica*, *Potentilla*, and *Taraxacum* are largely adaptive features of ancestral outcrossers, since plants of these three genera are highly apomictic in the north. The dioecy of *Antennaria* is also vestigial since northern *Antennaria* are not only apomictic but are high polyploids. Many additional examples could be cited. A similar situation seems to be present among our weedy flora. It is certainly not a coincidence that most of our outcrossed and usually self-incompatible weeds are perennial rather than annual or biennial, for example, *Sonchus arvensis*, *Cardaria*, *Linaria*, *Lactuca*, *Trifolium repens*, *T. hybridum*, and *T. pratense*. Similarly, perennial weeds like *Hypericum perforatum*, *Taraxacum*, and some species of *Hieracium* (which may be actively visited by insects), although they appear to be normally outcrossed, are in fact strongly apomictic. Outcrossing among weeds, therefore, appears to be at a selective disadvantage because when features promoting outcrossing are present, they are compensated for by perennity or by apomixis, both of which tend to ensure population constancy. That this "adaptive compensation" does in fact operate on a large scale among weeds is suggested by the fact that outcrossing is not associated as a rule with weeds that have short life cycles. Such weeds are normally self-pollinated and can therefore "afford" to have short life cycles as well as low chromosome numbers.

It is of interest to consider the possible reasons for the remarkable success of constant genetic systems in high latitude and weedy floras. Stebbins (57, pp. 176–79; 59) has stated that plant populations characterized by self-pollination or apomixis are usually found in temporary habitats, particularly in the case af annuals or short-lived perennials. Although annuals and short-lived perennials are not common in the arctic, the region contains a very high percentage of self-pollinated, apomictic (and polyploid) species, the majority of which are medium-lived perennials. Both boreal and arctic habitats are certainly not marginal or temporary since arctic environments date back at least to the late Pliocene and the boreal is undoubtedly much older. Likewise weedy environments are in my opinion relatively constant over large regions of the world (although they may be temporary in one small area). Mulligan (41) and others have shown that there are many different kinds of weedy environments, for example, lawns, roadsides, row-crop fields, grain fields, pastures, and so on and that each environment has its characteristic weeds. In my opinion, therefore, it is not the temporariness or the marginality but rather the recurrent restrictiveness of northern climate and the relative uniformity of the many types of weedy habitats that create conditions for the remarkable success of constant genetic systems in these environments. The identity of the limiting factor promoting genetic constancy in the northern floras may be low soil and air temperatures during the growing season. Low temperatures would result in selection favouring the correlation and completion of many types of biochemical reactions at temperatures which are minimal for the maintenance of life. It would be advantageous to such plants to acquire reproductive features which keep variability to a minimum. Among weedy floras the identity of the factors favouring population constancy would vary from one weedy habitat to another. Parenthetically, I should like to add that the probable reason why weeds are so common in temperate and tropical regions is that man himself has created weedy environments in those areas where ideal diploid hermaphrodites are common and serve as a rich reservoir for the production of weeds.

If the above hypothesis on the relationship between genetic systems and northern climate is correct, then pollen vectors which are so necessary for maintaining outcrossing reproductive systems of plants of tropical and temperate regions should have progressively less and in some instances no effect on plant adaptation in the higher latitudes. Thus although many arctic insects clearly depend on nectar- and pollen-producing, showy-flowered plants for survival, these plants may have little or no need for insects.

Hybridization between obviously different species as a source of genetic variability appears to be uncommon in the arctic. Few F_1 hybrids are known from the higher latitudes. The only example known to me of what appears to be introgression is between *Poa hartzii* and *P. glauca* from Ellesmere Island described by Savile (53). Most taxonomically difficult genera owe their complexity to apomixis. Intra-populational variation is extremely rare but known from *Saxifraga oppositifolia* (Savile 53). The genetic basis for variability in some classically difficult groups like *Stellaria longipes* and *Cerastium alpinum* has not yet been experimentally demonstrated.

Our understanding of the role of polyploidy in evolution is presently undergoing important changes mainly because of the discovery that genes can very frequently control chromosome pairing at meiosis (see previous discussion). Polyploids are known to be conservative and they do not seem to have the capacity to produce major new kinds of plants. Yet, many polyploids, for example *Dactylis glomerata* (Stebbins and Zohary, 60) and *Clarkia rhomboidea* (Mosquin, 40), are extremely variable and may have wide ranges. The extensive variability and distribution ranges of such polyploids appear to be due mainly to one or several of the following factors: (1) hybridization between polyploid races originating repeatedly from various geographical races of diploids, (2) repeated intergenomic exchange which results in new linkage relationships and new position effects, and (3) to the presence of a rich diversity of habitats which permit certain polyploid derivatives to adapt to a variety of conditions in which their parents could not grow. Such polyploids are frequently segmental alloploids (Stebbins, 57) and have wide ecological ranges of tolerance. It is probably of great significance that these polyploids have to my knowledge been found to be native to temperate regions which have great ecological diversity, rather than to the colder climates which are relatively uniform. It is only those polyploids that do not have the capacity or mechanism for giving rise to a wide range of variants that have been uniquely qualified for the colonization of the higher latitudes and of weedy environments. In northern and in man-made environments, polyploids decrease rather than increase the variability and the flexibility of the genetic system. Genic control of chromosome pairing as considered in the early part of this paper may be the vital factor partly responsible for maintaining the buffering and the consequent conservatism in northern and weedy polyploids. Genic diploidization, since it restores normal, diploid-like gametogenesis, ensures fertility. Once genic control of chromosome pairing develops, even segmental alloploids having grossly reorganized segments will become more conservative because crossing over between homologous segments, regardless of their position, will be prevented. I therefore feel that there is no experimental evidence whatsoever to support the widely popularized hypothesis that polyploids *per se* have greater ecological ranges of tolerances than diploids as suggested by Hagerup (26) and Löve & Löve (36). This is particularly so because both Hagerup and Löve & Löve were referring to high latitude and weedy polyploids. The reason that polyploids are widespread in northern and weedy environments is that polyploidy in these regions has a similar impact on the genetic system as have self-pollination and apomixis: it permits the perpetuation of a genetic system having narrow adaptational limits. Such polyploids have very wide distribution ranges because the narrow and relatively uniform boreal, arctic, and weedy environments are widespread.

If the hypothesis on the relation between genetic systems and environmental uniformity or restrictiveness is correct, then ecologists might use genetic systems of plants as clues to the nature of the environmental parameters in a habitat. After all, environments have been testing genetic systems for millions of years. If genetic systems encountered restrictiveness or uniformity they themselves would promote uniformity but if they encountered permissiveness they would promote variability. It would not be at all surprising if botanists of the future were to find that the plants inhabiting specific ecological zones would have significantly different levels of genetic variability, for example the tree, shrub, and herb strata in a forest, the various ecological zones of sea and lake shores, or the altitudinal or edaphic zones in physiographically variable regions. It is of interest that Gustafsson (25) and Johnson and Packer (29) have already found such correlations between ecological zones and chromosomes characteristics, particularly polyploidy. No doubt other characteristics listed in Fig. 1 would show similar changes in frequency with different ecological conditions. Should such correlations prove to be widespread in the plant kingdom, then they will unquestionably be of great practical and theoretical value to ecologists and to other population biologists.

When we consider the immense amount of diversity among higher plants stemming from ideal diploid hermaphrodites, it is surprising that the main colonizers of widespread weedy and arctic habitats have the kinds of genetic systems that lead toward population uniformity; this, despite the presence of potential insect pollinators or wind pollination in both areas. One can only conclude that the kinds of mechanisms which preserve population uniformity (and so lead to evolutionary dead ends), impart superior adaptative properties to plants in these habitats. The *absence* of diploid outcrossers in the arctic, and the compensation for outcrossing among weeds by perennity and apomixis (as considered previously), also suggest that a high level of genetic variability is not adaptive in boreal, arctic, and weedy habitats. If self-pollination and apomixis in the arctic were simply devices to ensure seed set, then these devices would not be so common in temperate weedy habitats where pollinators are very common and where full seed set can therefore be readily attained by outcrossing. Also, if seed set were of primary importance to arctic plants, then polyploidy which is so common in the north would require a special explanation. It is true that self-pollinated and apomictic plants would have a better chance for long-distance establishment, but such establishment is, I feel, only a minor episode in maintaining the extensive distributions of boreal, arctic, and weedy floras. What *is* important is the hereditary capacity to use some reproductive device or combination of devices to preserve a highly adapted physiological system once such a system has been discovered by mutation and recombination.

If natural selection favours progressively less genetic variability with increases in latitude, then the evolutionary potential of plants of lower latitude floras will be greatest, while the capacity to produce new species and genera in the higher latitudes will become severely restricted. Loss of a great deal of evolutionary potential is, therefore, the price of adaption to our latitudes. This loss would explain two well-known facts about our native flora. One is the singular lack of endemic genera in our area, in contrast to climatically unique areas of more southern latitudes. The other is the notable lack of genetic variability within many of our species, even though they have extensive circumboreal and circumpolar distributions. Many Canadian species and genera are conservative and relatively static in evolution because they have for the most part lost the dynamic qualities of ideal diploid hermaphrodites. This does not mean that evolution of plants in the higher latitudes or in weedy floras has stopped, but only that it proceeds at a relatively slow rate. Northern species of the genera *Salix*, *Betula, Carex,* and various Ericaceae, Orchidaceae, Liliaceae, and others therefore give the appearance of being or are known to be relatively ancient. In the future, new species and genera suitable for colonizing the boreal and arctic zones are more likely to originate from variable temperate plants than from the genetically quite constant populations already growing in northern regions.

ACKNOWLEDGMENTS

It is my pleasure to thank C. Frankton, H. Lewis, G. A. Mulligan, T. Rajhathy, P. H. Raven, and D. B. O. Savile for their numerous helpful criticisms and suggestions concerning the manuscript. G. A. Mulligan kindly permitted me to use some unpublished information on the Canadian Cruciferae and W. G. Dore helped in scoring many of the grasses for Fig. 3. Special thanks go to D. B. O. Savile with whom I had many useful and stimulating discussions on morphology and floral biology of arctic plants. Many of the staff of the Plant Research Institute provided information and opinions on diverse groups of plants and influenced the ideas expressed in this paper.

REFERENCES

1. AXELROD, D. I. 1952. A theory of angiosperm evolution. Evolution 6: 29–60.
2. ——— 1959. Poleward migration of early angiosperm floras. Science *130:* 203–207.
3. BABCOCK, E. B. 1947. The genus *Crepis,* I and II. Univ. Calif. Publ. Bot. *21, 22:* 1–1030.
4. BALDWIN, W. K. W. 1958. Plants of the clay belt of northern Ontario and Quebec. Nat. Mus. Bull. No. 156. 324 pp.
5. BAKER, H. G. 1959. Reproductive methods as factors in speciation in flowering plants. Cold Spring Harbor Symposia Quant. Biol. *24:* 177–191.
6. BATEMAN, A. J. 1952. Self-incompatibility systems in angiosperms. Heredity 6: 285–310.
7. ——— 1955. Self-incompatibility systems in angiosperms: III, Cruciferae. Heredity 9: 53–68.
8. BINGHAM, M. T. 1939. Orchids of Michigan. Cranbrook Inst., Bull. No. 15. 87 pp.
9. BUDD, A. C. 1957. The wild plants of the Canadian prairies. Can. Dept. Agr., Publ. No. 983. 348 pp.
10. CALDER, J. A., and R. L. TAYLOR. Flora of the Queen Charlotte Islands: I, Systematics of the Vascular Plants (in manuscript).
11. CHAMBERS, K. L. 1955. A biosystematic study of the annual species of *Microseris.* Contr. Dudley Herb. *4:* 207–312.
12. CORNER, E. J. H. 1954. The evolution of tropical rain forest, 34–46. *In*

J. S. Huxley, A. C. Hardy, and E. B. Ford, eds., Evolution as a Process. G. Allen & Unwin Ltd., London. 367 pp.

13. —— 1964. The Life of Plants. Weidenfeld and Nicolson, London. 315 pp.

14. CROWE, L. K. 1964. The evolution of outbreeding in plants: I, The angiosperms. Heredity *19*: 435–457.

15. DARLINGTON, C. D. 1958. Evolution of Genetic Systems. Oliver and Boyd, Edinburgh, London. 265 pp.

16. —— 1963. Chromosome Botany and the Origins of Cultivated Plants. G. Allen & Unwin Ltd., London. 231 pp.

17. DAVIES, E. W. 1956. Cytology, evolution and origin of the aneuploid series in the genus *Carex*. Hereditas *42*: 349–365.

18. DELEVORYAS, T. 1962. Morphology and Evolution of Fossil Plants. Holt, Rinehart & Winston, New York. 189 pp.

19. DOWNES, J. A. 1962. What is an arctic insect? Can. Entomologist *94*: 143–162.

20. —— 1964. Arctic insects and their environment. Can. Entomologist *96*: 279–307.

21. —— 1965. Adaptations of insects in the arctic. Ann. Rev. Entomol. *10*: 257–274.

22. EAST, E. M. 1940. The distribution of self-sterility in the flowering plants. Proc. Amer. Philos. Soc. *82*: 449–518.

23. FRYXELL, P. A. 1957. Mode of reproduction of higher plants. Botan. Rev. *23*: 135–233.

24. GUSTAFSSON, A. 1946–7. Apomixis in Higher Plants. Parts I–III. Lunds Univ. Arsskr. N. R. Avd. 2, 42–44: 1–370.

25. —— 1948. Polyploidy, life form, and vegetative reproduction. Hereditas *34*: 1–22.

26. HAGERUP, O. 1932. Über Polyploidie in Beziehung zu Klima, Okologie, und Phylogenie. Hereditas *16*: 19–40.

27. HICKS, G. 1929. Cytological studies in *Cyperus, Eleocharis, Dulichium,* and *Eriophorum*. Botan. Gaz. *88*: 1132–1149.

28. HJELMQVIST, H. 1948. Studies on the floral morphology and phylogeny of the Amentiferae. Botan. Nat. Suppl. *2*: 1–171.

29. JOHNSON, A. W., and J. G. PACKER. 1965. Polyploidy and environment in arctic Alaska. Science *148*: 237–239.

30. KIMBER, G. 1961. The basis for diploid-like meiotic behavior in polyploid cotton. Nature *191*: 98–100.

31. KIMBER, G., and R. RILEY. 1963. The relationships of the diploid progenitors of hexaploid wheat. Can. J. Genet. Cytol. *5*: 83–88.

32. LAWRENCE, G. H. M. 1951. Taxonomy of Vascular Plants. Macmillan Co., New York. 823 pp.

33. Lewis, D. 1942. The evolution of sex in flowering plants. Biol. Rev. *17*: 46–67.

34. —— 1954. Comparative incompatibility in angiosperms and fungi. Advances in Genet. *6*: 235–285.

35. LEWIS, H. 1953. The mechanism of evolution in the genus *Clarkia*. Evolution 7: 1–20.

36. LÖVE, A., and D. LÖVE. 1949. The geobotanical significance of polyploidy: I, Polyploidy and latitude. Portugaliae Acta Biol. A. 273–352.

37. McALPINE, J. F. 1965. Observations on anthophilous diptera at Lake Hazen, Ellesmere Island. Can. Field Nat. 79: 247–252.

38. MOORE, D. M., and H. LEWIS. 1965. The evolution of self-pollination in *Clarkia xantiana*. Evolution *19*: 104–114.

39. MOORE, R. J. and J. A. CALDER. 1964. Some chromosome numbers of *Carex* species of Canada and Alaska. Can. J. Botan. *42*: 1387–1391.

40. MOSQUIN, T. 1964. Chromosomal repatterning in *Clarkia rhomboidea* as

evidence for post-Pleistocene changes in distribution. Evolution *18*: 12–25.

41. MULLIGAN, G. A. 1965. Colonization by higher plants in Canada. *In* H. G. Baker and G. L. Stebbins, eds., The Genetics of Colonizing Species. Academic Press, New York. 562 pp.

42. PORSILD, A. E. 1957. Illustrated flora of the Canadian Arctic Archipelago. Nat. Mus. Bull. No. 146.

43. RAUP, H. M. 1930. The pollinization of *Habenaria obtusata*. Rhodora *32*: 88–89.

44. RAVEN, P. H. 1962. The systematics of *Oenothera* subgenus *Chylismia*. Univ. Calif. Publ. Botan. *34*: 1–122.

45. REESE, G. 1961. Karyotype and plant geography, 895–900. *In* Recent Advances in Botany, Univ. Toronto Press. *1*: 1–947.

46. RICHARDS, P. W. 1957. The Tropical Rain Forest: Cambridge Univ. Press. 450 pp.

47. RILEY, R. 1960. The diploidization of polyploid wheat. Heredity *15*: 407–429.

48. —— 1965. Cytogenetics and the evolution of wheat, 103–122. *In* J. HUTCHINSON, ed., Essays on Crop Plant Evolution. Cambridge Univ. Press. 204 pp.

49. RILEY, R., and C. KEMPANNA. 1963. The homeologous nature of the non-homologous meiotic pairing in *Triticum aestivum* deficient for chromosome V (5B). Heredity *18*: 287–306.

50. RILEY, R., and V. CHAPMAN. 1964. Cytological determination of the homeology of chromosomes of *Triticum aestivum*. Nature *203*: 156–158.

51. SAVILE, D. B. O. 1959. The botany of Somerset Island, District of Franklin. Can. J. Botan. *37*: 959–1002.

52. —— 1961. The botany of the northwestern Queen Elizabeth Islands. Can. J. Botan. *39*: 909–942.

53. —— 1965. General ecology and vascular plants of the Hazen Camp area. Arctic *17*: 237–258.

54. SNOGERUP, S. 1963. Studies in the genus *Juncus* III: Observations on the diversity of chromosome numbers. Botan. Notiser *116*: 142–156.

55. SOPER, J. H. 1949. Vascular plants of Southern Ontario. Univ. Toronto and Federation Ont. Naturalists, Toronto. 95 pp.

56. SPRAGUE, E. F. 1962. Pollination and evolution in *Pedicularis* (Scrophulariaceae). Aliso *5*: 181–209.

57. STEBBINS, G. L. 1950. Variation and Evolution in Plants. Columbia Univ. Press, New York. 643 pp.

58. —— 1957. Self-fertilization and population variability in the higher plants. Amer. Nat. *91*: 337–354.

59. —— 1958. Longevity, habitat and release of genetic variability in the higher plants. Cold Spring Harbour Symposia Quant. Biol. *23*: 365–378.

60. STEBBINS, G. L., and D. ZOHARY. 1959. Cytogenetic and evolutionary studies in the genus *Dactylis*: I, Morphology, distribution and interrelationship of the diploid subspecies. Univ. Calif. Publ. Botany *31*: 1–40.

61. SWANSON, C. P. 1957. Cytology and cytogenetics. Prentice-Hall Inc., N. J. 596 pp.

62. WAHL, H. A. 1940. Chromosome numbers and meiosis in the genus *Carex*. Amer. J. Botany *27*: 458–470.

63. WESTERGAARD, M. 1958. The mechanism of sex determination in dioecious flowering plants. Advances in Genet. *9*: 217–281.

64. WHITEHOUSE, H. L. K. 1959. Cross- and self-fertilization in plants, 207–261. *In* P. R. Bell, ed., Darwin's Biological Work. Cambridge Univ. Press. 343 pp.

65. YAMPOLSKY, C., and H. YAMPOLSKY. 1922. Distribution of sex forms in the phanerogamic flora. Bibl. Genet. *3*: 1–62.

J. C. RITCHIE

Aspects of the Late-Pleistocene History of the Canadian Flora

THE CONTRIBUTION OF STUDIES of late-Pleistocene flora is of limited relevance to the basic question posed in this colloquium—what is the origin of the Canadian flora? It is fairly clear that most elements in the present flora have existed in North America throughout the Quaternary, and their origins must be traced in data from late Tertiary deposits. It is equally clear that the facts available are inadequate even to approach the question of late Tertiary and early Quaternary floristic history. However, there is a contribution to be made to floristic geography by Pleistocene studies, in that the contemporary distribution of the flora can be understood in part in terms of patterns of immigration into deglaciated land areas.

While gaps remain, the general configurations of present-day plant distributions are well known, and Porsild (25) has provided a clear preliminary summary of the main floristic elements of our flora. Further, several notable attempts have been made to reconstruct hypothetical sequences of re-immigration, or to propose survival phenomena, to account for certain chorological patterns in the flora (Braun, 3; Fernald, 14; Hulten, 19; Marie-Victorin, 23; Raup, 26; and others).

It is perhaps appropriate now, if not essential, to assemble the factual record of late-Pleistocene flora, and to attempt to reconstruct the past on the basis of fact alone. The exemplary studies of Godwin (18) and his colleagues might serve to point the way for studies of the history of the Canadian flora. The main sources of direct information about Holocene floras are records of plant macrofossil and pollen assemblages. In general, primary limnic deposits are the most reliable repositories for these subfossils, but bog, and even alluvial deposits also yield useful data. Investigations of deposits bearing such material for analysis have a long and fruitful history in Northwest Europe, the Soviet Union, and elsewhere in the Old World, and the last decade has seen a notable intensification and refinement of these studies in the United States. In Canada, as Terasmae (32) has pointed out, such investigations have lagged somewhat, and they continue to be pursued somewhat fitfully and without adequate interdisciplinary co-ordination. It would perhaps be appropriate here to recommend our new botanical organization to nurture a co-ordinated resurgence in Canadian biogeography, with particular emphasis on Quaternary history.

It might be appropriate to outline briefly what can be expected of botanical studies of the late-Pleistocene, particularly in their application to problems of floristic geography. The information which is relevant to floristics can be abstracted at three levels.

First, there is the floristic record of what actually grew at a site, derived mainly from occurrences of large fragments or organs of plants, or less commonly, occurrences of large pollen grains or spores poorly adapted for dispersal. These are unquestionably the most valuable data for floristic geography, but they are seldom available, partly because limnic and other deposits rich in macrofossils are somewhat rare, but mainly because there is insufficient investigation of this kind.

Secondly, relevant data can be derived from reconstructions of Holocene vegetation. These are based largely on rather loose interpretations of pollen spectra, usually summarized as relative frequencies of pollen and spore types. The evidence adduced here is seldom of *direct* floristic significance, but often it provides data that strengthen, or possibly erode explanatory hypotheses. However, palynological analyses of sediments in extra-tropical regions of the northern hemisphere seldom yield assemblages of more than one hundred pollen types, of which perhaps only one quarter can be identified with certainty to species level. Thus while we assume reasonably, that at least in forested regions the dominant elements of the vegetation are represented in pollen spectra, we can hardly expect to find evidence in one site for much more than five per cent of the total flora. Nonetheless, it is likely that the post-glacial history of our flora will be based almost entirely on the results of palynological analyses. While one can search hopefully for rich deposits of plant macrofossils in early Holocene (late-glacial) sediments, post-glacial deposits seldom yield many remnants of terrestrial plants. It should be noted also that pollen analysis has several old, acute, and yet unsolved problems of its own, and until some progress has been made towards resolving them, one should view the published interpretations of pollen diagrams with the utmost caution. It is possible that the limitations of the method will be more exactly known when investigations along three lines of enquiry have matured—studies of pollen sedimentation rates in limnic deposits (Davis and Deevey, 8), of the relations between contemporary pollen spectra and landform-vegetation regions (Ritchie and Lichti-Federovich, 29), and of the differential preservation of pollen in lake sediments (Sangster and Dale, 31).

The final source of relevant data is paleoecology, and its contribution to historical plant geography is the least direct. The ultimate *desideratum* of late-Pleistocene studies, and it can be realized only under conditions of full interdisciplinary collaboration, is to assemble all possible analyses of chronologically and stratigraphically correlated biotas and sediments and to draw inferences about past environments. Certain substantial *a priori* assumptions are involved here, largely stemming from the methodology of geology, and the most that one can hope for is an accumulation of biological, geological, and physico-chemical data with considerable ecological concordance. The usefulness of paleoecology to floristic geography is in providing reconstructions of the possible biotic and abiotic settings; the danger is to base reconstructions of past floras on paleoecological inferences, thus slipping into a familiar circuity of argument and reasoning.

I propose to restrict my discussion to one of the four main phytogeographical regions of Canada, for various reasons which will emerge below. For many biogeographical purposes, and specifically for late-Pleistocene studies, we may recognize four general regions in Canada —the Arctic, the Cordilleran region, the Western Interior, and the Eastern region. I propose to examine here certain aspects of the late-Pleistocene history of the Western Interior of Canada, mainly because it lies within my own bailiwick, but also because the other three areas present a picture at present which is too complicated and confused, or, in the case of the Arctic, too inadequately investigated, to permit any clear generalizations. The contemporary and sub-fossil pollen assemblages from the Western Interior (approximately from western Ontario to the foothills, following the suggestion of Warkentin, 36) are composed of relatively few types, yielding simple but apparently informative pollen diagrams, whereas both the eastern and cordilleran floras have a profusion of anemophilous trees, often with indistinguishable pollen between closely related but ecologically distinct species, posing acute problems in interpretation. On the other hand, some of the difficulties of interpretation of Arctic data are caused by the paucity of pollen types recorded (Livingston, 22, Colinvaux, 6).

The area to be considered (Fig. 1) lies at the conjunction of three major floristic provinces—the Northern Conifer Forest, the Eastern Deciduous Forest, and the Grasslands as defined by Gleason and Cronquist (17). We shall examine the botanical findings recorded from various sites in the Western Interior of Canada (sites 1–7, Fig. 1), suggest an interpretation in terms of vegetation history, draw some comparisons with geologically similar sites in Minnesota (sites 8–12), and finally, suggest the broad outlines of possible floristic history.

It is unfortunate that there is still some uncertainty about the glacial geology of the area, but we can suggest with reasonable assurance that the sites shown in Fig. 1 lie close to, or within the land area exposed during the Two Creeks interstadial, and most have been ice-free since that time. Following Christiansen (5) we can show the approximate position of the ice front at the Condie re-advance, which is tentatively correlated with Valders (Christiansen, 4), and the suggested position of the Valders ice front in western Ontario (Zoltai, 41 and 42). However, the position of the Valders ice front in the region of the southern extension of Glacial Lake Agassiz II remains in doubt (Elson, 9, 11, 12).

MISSOURI COTEAU SITES—GRASSLAND REGION

There have been several investigations in the last decade of fossiliferous sediments on or near the Missouri Coteau, in both Saskatchewan (Kupsch, 21, Ritchie and de Vries, 28, and Terasmae, 33, unpubl.) and North Dakota (Tuthill *et al.*, 34). Two sites will be discussed here—Hafichuk and Crestwynd—sites 2 and 3 respectively in Fig. 1. Both occur in kettle depressions of hummocky, disintegration moraine, well within the northern extension of the Grasslands region. The Hafichuk site (described in detail by de Vries, 35, and Ritchie and de Vries, 28) was an excavation at the edge of a depression and revealed late-glacial gyttja quite close to the ground surface (depth of 3 m).

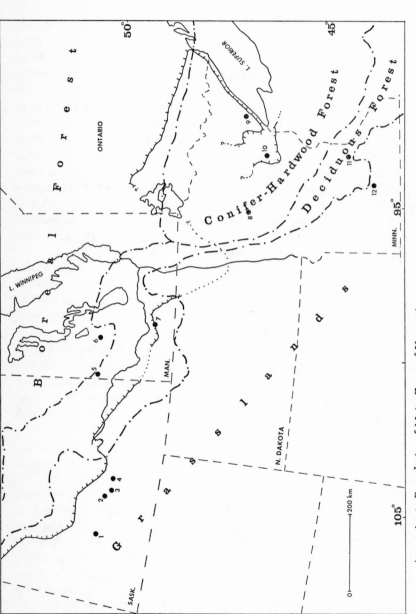

FIGURE 1. The sites referred to in the text are as follows: 1—Herbert; 2—Hafichuk; 3—Crestwynd; 4—Scrimbit; 5—Russel; 6—Riding Mountain; 7—Glenboro; 8—Series of sites studied by McAndrews (24); 9—Weber Lake by Fries (15); 10—Spider Creek by Baker (2); 11—Kirchner Marsh by Wright *et al.* (40); and 12—Madelia by Jelgersma (20).

- · - · - Approximate Boundaries of Major Zones of Vegetation

||||| Valders Ice Front (Ontario) Condie Ice Front (Saskatchewan)

The Crestwynd site was cored with a piston sampler attached to a powered auger, and yielded a long section (20 m) ending in till, but with only the middle 4 m yielding samples suitable for pollen analysis. The Hafichuk pollen spectra (Fig. 2) indicate an assemblage dominated by *Picea*, with considerable relative amounts of *Populus, Salix, Shepherdia canadensis*, and herbs, chiefly *Artemisia*. De Vries (35) identified a relatively rich assemblage of macrofossils in the middle levels of the section, with many species characteristic, at present, of both boreal and temperate regions, for example, *Picea glauca, P. mariana, Juniperus communis, Typha, Zannichellia, Triglochin maritima, Elodea, Scirpus, Lemna, Spirodela, Wolffia, Populus tremuloides, P. balsamifera, P. deltoides, Ceratophyllum demersum, Subularia aquatica, Rosa blanda*, and others. The Crestwynd site (Fig. 2) appears to include only the early post-glacial, and indeed the relative ages, levels, and topographical positions of the sediments at the Hafichuk and Crestwynd sites might conform to the hypothesis of Tuthill *et al.* (34), who suggest that certain late-glacial sediments in North Dakota on the Missouri Coteau were accumulated in ice-walled lakes. The Crestwynd assemblages (Fig. 2), with various minor features of interest discussed elsewhere (Ritchie and Lichti-Federovich, 30), resembles closely what we interpret as a grassland type, and it is possible that the trend from spruce-dominated late-glacial assemblages to early post-glacial grassland-type assemblages was fairly general in this area, since it is indicated also in the diagrams of Terasmae from the Herbert (*in* Kupsch, 21) and Scrimbit Farm sites (Terasmae, unpubl.).

TIGER HILLS—DECIDUOUS FOREST REGION

A section of limnic sediment, recovered from a small lake in the terminal moraine hills immediately south of Glenboro, Manitoba, reveals an informative sequence of pollen assemblages. These are shown in a condensed form in Fig. 3, and they will be reported and described in more detail in a later publication. The site lies in an area of low hills, partly farmed, otherwise dominated by an aspen–oak community, with small amounts of birch, elm, and Manitoba maple.

The lowest levels of the section, yielding a Carbon-14 age determination of 12,800 ± 300 years BP, show a pollen assemblage very similar to that recorded from the Hafichuk site, and indeed show strong similarities to what is becoming the typical late-glacial spectrum for sites in the entire midwestern region of North America. It will be necessary

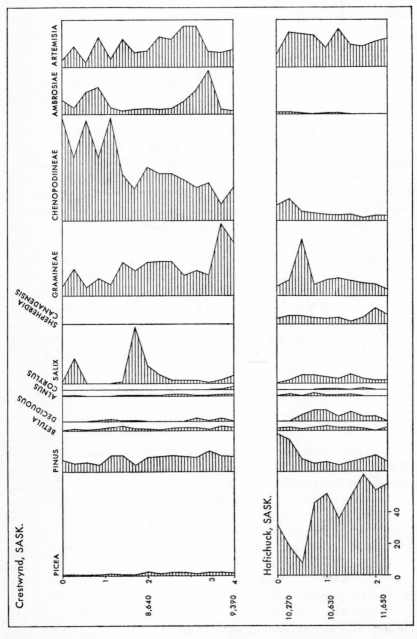

FIGURE 2. Simplified pollen diagrams from two dated sections of limnic sediment, at Crestwynd and Hafichuk, Saskatchewan, showing the relative amounts of the main pollen types. The scale on the left shows only the extent of the section and not the levels from the surface.

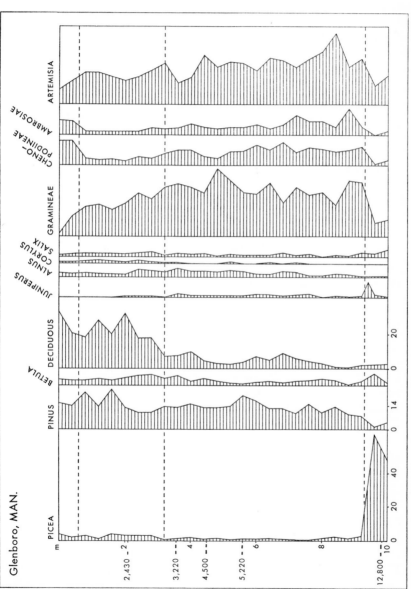

Figure 3. A simplified, preliminary pollen diagram from a 10 m section of limnic sediment from small lake near Glenboro, Manitoba. On the left are shown the C-14 age determinations of sediment samples in the years BP. The column "Deciduous" includes *Quercus, Fraxinus,* and *Ulmus* with any angiosperm trees except *Betula*. The values are percentages of the total pollen sum, minus aquatics. The broken lines indicate the limits of the four pollen assemblages distinguished in this diagram.

to provide further Carbon-14 determinations and pollen analysis from sections recovered from other lakes in the Tiger Hills, but this preliminary finding suggests that the Darlingford–Edinburg–Holt moraine system (Elson, 10) does not mark the Valders re-advance. The second pollen assemblage in this section (Fig. 3), immediately above the spruce-dominated, late-glacial zone, is characterized by high relative values of non-arboreal pollen types, conforming with what we (Ritchie, 27) have suggested elsewhere as a grassland spectrum. At about the 3 m level, dated approximately 3000 BP, there is a change, and an assemblage prevails with relatively high values of *Quercus*, associated with *Fraxinus* and *Ulmus*. We suggest tentatively that this assemblage might be interpreted in terms of either an oak–savannah community, or an aspen–oak forest. A final change in the relative amounts of the assemblage components can be detected about the 30 cm level, and we ascribe the increases in Ambrosieae and Chenopodiineae and decline in native grasses to the influences of settlement. The increase in the relative amounts of deciduous forest types might reflect a spread of forest as settlement put a check to the widespread fires, or it might be a reflection of the decline in the relative amount of herbaceous pollen types in the pollen rain with the spread of agriculture.

RIDING MOUNTAIN AREA—MIXED BOREAL REGION

Referring briefly to an earlier, already published study (Ritchie, 27), Fig. 4 depicts a composite, simplified diagram from three sites in the Riding Mountain National Park of Manitoba, and one can detect at least four fairly distinctive pollen assemblages. Again the lowest is a *Picea–Artemisia* type, followed by a grassland assemblage in which were recorded individual, large pollen grains of species confined today to the grasslands of the midwest. The grassland type is replaced by a vegetation dominated by birch and oak, and, we suggest, poplar; and finally the spruce–birch–alder assemblage appears and persists throughout the upper strata.

In the light of this subfossil record, we might attempt a preliminary, highly tentative conspectus of the floristic history of the Western Interior of Canada. In doing so, we will include for comparative purposes some of the recent findings of the active Limnological Research Center at the University of Minnesota, directed by Dr. H. J. Wright, Jr.

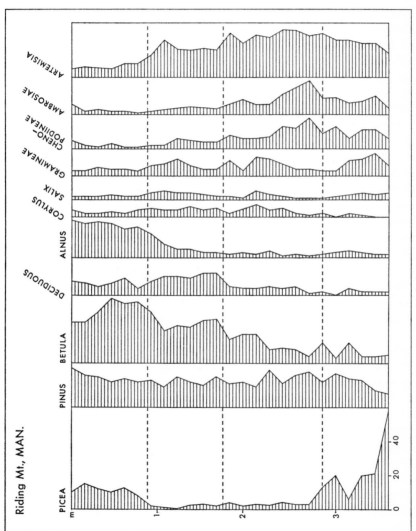

FIGURE 4. A simplified pollen diagram from Riding Mountain, Manitoba, showing the relative amounts of the main pollen types. The broken lines indicate the limits of the four pollen assemblages distinguished in this diagram.

THE LATE-GLACIAL FLORA

The earliest late-glacial pollen assemblages show remarkable quali-
tative and quantitative uniformity over a wide area, including Saskatchewan, Manitoba, Minnesota, Wisconsin, and Michigan (cf. West,
37, and Andersen, 1). Relatively few studies of macrofossils have been
published, but the findings of Farnham, McAndrews, and Wright (13)
and Ritchie and de Vries (28) confirm the data of the pollen analysis
in showing a mixture of plants of boreal and temperate affinities.
However, Baker (2) has recorded arctic-subarctic species from late-
glacial sediments at Spider Creek, St. Louis County, Minnesota,
namely, *Dryas integrifolia, Salix herbacea, Vaccinium uliginosum* var.
alpinum, Potentilla nivea, Rhododendron lapponicum, and *Carex capil-
laris.* Thus the floristic record for the late-glacial in the midwest,
although it is still very meagre, consists of a variety of plants whose
contemporary geographical affinities are primarily North American,
wide-ranging, boreal, temperate, or in a few cases arctic.

The related problems of interpreting these assemblages in terms of
vegetation, and finally, of what paleoecological inferences might be
drawn, can be considered only briefly here. Indeed, there is still too
little information available to permit any definite reconstructions of
late-glacial vegetation, far less to suggest what the climate might have
been, unless we forswear the injunction of Ernst Mayr that "the basis
of all scientific interpretation is the rule of parsimony, which demands
in each case the simplest explanation consistent with the facts." It is
unlikely that any vegetation exists today on a regional scale which is
similar to the late-glacial communities. One suspects that the late-
glacial spruce-dominated communities were youthful and primeval,
whereas the modern boreal forest is a patchwork of decadent and
disturbed vegetation, with pine, birch, and aspen given the advantage
over spruce. However, as I (27) have suggested elsewhere, one can
find particular ecological situations, usually where geologically young
sites are exposed, which present a pattern of vegetation similar to
what is suggested by the late-glacial spectra.

It is likely that a persistent search for further sites of sediments
rich in macrofossils will result in a growing list of late-glacial plants.
For the present we might offer the speculative comment, in no sense
original, that many of our transcontinental boreal, temperate, and in
some cases arctic species, re-occupied Canada in late-glacial times,
migrating from southern refugia. The specific record of *Dryas integrifolia* by Baker (2) offers the "fossil proof" that was lacking when

Porsild (25) wrote that it "was widespread in pre-Pleistocene time, and survived the ice age in close proximity to the ice fronts. Following the retreat of the ice it rapidly reoccupied the land, only to be destroyed again in the southern part by the advancing forests."

POST-GLACIAL FLORAS

We should concede at the outset that the few facts available to date confirm the hypothesis set out by Gleason (16) in a brilliant essay, based entirely on contemporary chorology, outlining the vegetational and floristic history of the American midwest. A comparison of the data from the sites marked in Fig. 1 shows a distinct difference between the post-glacial sequences to the west and east of the Red River Valley. The post-glacial changes to the east, in Minnesota and adjacent Ontario, have been discussed fully in the light of recent data by Wright (38, 39). He (38) outlines the change from late- to early-post-glacial times as "a boreal spruce forest gave way through rapid transitional changes to a mixed deciduous forest, which has persisted with relatively little change since that time." He suggests that birch and pine, in contrast to spruce, were restricted during the Wisconsin glaciation to eastern refugia in the Appalachians. The subsequent spread and prevalence of elm- and oak-dominated forests is accounted for in terms of relatively slow migration rates.

The pollen assemblages reported so far from west of the Red River Valley show a different post-glacial succession. The early post-glacial period in the area of southern Manitoba and Saskatchewan was characterized by the disappearance (almost entirely) of the conifer forest, as well as all continuous forest communities, and the extension from the southwest of what appears to have been a grassland cover. The occasional occurrences of pollen of such prairie types as *Phlox hoodii, Sphaeralcea coccinea,* and *Shepherdia argentea* support this interpretation. Thus we are provided with a reasonable basis for the contention, put forward by Gleason (16), that many of the isolated occurrences of western species in such forested regions as the Ohio Valley, the northern Great Lakes area, and even in the northern boreal forest are relict from the early post-glacial period. However, it is evident that since we can expect little assistance from macrofossil records in working out this post-glacial assemblage, further critical palynological studies will be needed to elucidate the floristics of this section of time. One of the most significant differences between post-glacial spectra west of the Red River Valley and those from the entire eastern region of North America is in the relative amounts of *Pinus* and *Betula*. Neither has formed a significant element in any post-glacial assemblage in Manitoba and Saskatchewan and it is likely that pine was never common in the post-glacial. Of course the recent re-interpretation of certain post-glacial spectra from eastern North America by Davis (7) has put in question the widely and rather uncritically accepted reconstruction of a Pine Period.

The final pollen assemblage in this western area, dated tentatively from approximately 3,500 BP, suggests a retreat of the grassland, replaced in part by deciduous forest types, particularly *Quercus* and *Betula*. One assumes also the presence of *Populus*; although it is rarely recorded in *post-glacial* sections, it has occurred in substantial relative amounts in late-glacial material along with small amounts of *Ulmus*, *Tilia*, and *Fraxinus*. The pollen diagrams by McAndrews (24) from northern Minnesota suggest that this intrusion of deciduous forest elements was along the Red River Valley.

Thus the late-Pleistocene history of the flora of the Western Interior of Canada will probably unfold—and it should be emphasized that the greater part of the work remains to be done—as follows:

1. An initial, relatively rapid immigration from the south of a fairly rich, mixed, transcontinental flora following ice disintegration, made up of floral elements which later differentiated into low arctic, boreal, and temperate groups depending upon the particular reaction of their ecological amplitude with the changing environment.

2. An intrusion northward and eastward of a western plains flora into the areas which were forested in the late-glacial period. Only careful investigations in the future will reveal the exact extent of this early, post-glacial, grassland region.

3. A reappearance in southern Manitoba and Saskatchewan of deciduous forest elements, some migrating southward from the conifer forest to the immediate north (*Betula*) and others extending north and west from the eastern deciduous forests.

The foregoing might appear a somewhat conservative resumé, and it certainly proposes nothing that is particularly novel to the phyto-geography of Canada. However, I submit that these propositions are commensurate with the facts at hand.

Provided certain preliminary work is completed so that pollen spectra can be interpreted with rather less uncertainty than at present, it is clear that some of the major problems of late-Pleistocene floristics in other parts of Canada will be resolved by pollen and macrofossil analysis of limnic and other sediments.

ACKNOWLEDGMENTS

The original investigations of the author referred to above were supported by grants from the National Science Foundation (Grant 23092) and the National Research Council of Canada (Grant T-1443). I wish to thank my colleague Mrs. Sigrid Lichti-Federovich for her advice and assistance in preparing this contribution.

REFERENCES

1. ANDERSEN, S. T. 1954. A late-glacial pollen diagram from southern Michigan, U.S.A. Danmarks geol. Underselse *80*: 140–155.
2. BAKER, R. G. 1964. Late-Wisconsin Glacial Geology and Vegetation: History of the Alborn Area, St. Louis County, Minnesota. M.Sc. thesis, Univ. Minnesota.
3. BRAUN, E. L. 1955. The phytogeography of unglaciated eastern United States and its interpretation. Botan. Rev. *21*: 297–375.
4. CHRISTIANSEN, E. A. 1960. Geology and ground-water resources of the Regina area of Saskatchewan. Sask. Res. Council, Geol. Div. No. 2. 72 pp.
—— 1965. Ice Frontal Positions in Saskatchewan. Sask. Res. Council, Map 2.
6. COLINVAUX, P. A. 1964. The environment of the Bering land bridge. Ecol. Monographs *34*: 297–329.
7. DAVIS, M. B. 1963. On the theory of pollen analysis. Am. J. Sci. *261*: 897–912.
8. DAVIS, M. B., and E. S. DEEVEY. 1964. Pollen accumulation rates: Estimates from late-glacial sediment of Rogers Lake. Science *145*: 1293–1295.
9. ELSON, J. A. 1957. Lake Agassiz and the Mankato–Valders problem. Science *126*: 992–1002.
10. —— 1958. Pleistocene history of southwestern Manitoba. N. Dakota Geol. Survey, Misc. Ser. *10*: 62–73.
11. ELSON, J. A. 1961. Soils of the Lake Agassiz region, 51–79. *In* R. F. Leggett, ed., Soils in Canada. Univ. Toronto Press.
12. —— History of Glacial Lake Agassiz. *In* J. R. Lowther, comp., Problems of the Pleistocene and Arctic, Publ. McGill Univ. Mus. *2*: 1–16.
13. FARNHAM, R. S., J. H. McANDREWS, and H. E. WRIGHT, JR. 1964. A late-Wisconsin buried soil near Aikin, Minnesota, and its paleo-botanical setting. Am. J. Sci. *262*: 393–412.
14. FERNALD, M. L. 1925. Persistence of plants in unglaciated areas of boreal America. Mem. Am. Acad. *15*: 241–342.
15. FRIES, M. 1962. Pollen profiles of Late-Pleistocene and Recent Sediments from Weber Lake, Minnesota. Ecology *43*: 295–308.
16. GLEASON, H. A. 1922. The vegetational history of the Middle West. Assoc. Am. Geogr. Ann. *12*: 39–85.
17. GLEASON, H. A., and A. CRONQUIST. 1964. The Natural Geography of Plants. Columbia Univ. Press, New York. 420 pp.
18. GODWIN, H. 1956. The History of the British Flora. Cambridge Univ. Press. 384 pp.
19. HULTEN, E. 1937. Outline of the History of Arctic and Boreal Biota during the Quaternary Period. Bokförlags Aktiebolaget Thule, Stockholm. 168 pp.

20. JELGERSMA, S.   1962.   A late-glacial pollen diagram from Madelia, south-central Minnesota. Am. J. Sci. *260*: 522–529.
21. KUPSCH, W. O.   1960.   Radiocarbon-dated organic sediment near Herbert, Saskatchewan. Am. J. Sci. *258*: 282–292.
22. LIVINGSTONE, D. A.   1955.   Pollen profiles from arctic Alaska. Ecology *36*: 587–600.
23. MARIE–VICTORIN, Fr.   1938.   Phytogeographical problems of eastern Canada. Am. Midl. Nat. *19*: 489–558.
24. MCANDREWS, J. H.   1962.   Post-glacial Vegetation History of the Prairie-Forest Transition of Northwestern Minnesota. Ph.D. thesis, Univ. Minnesota.
25. PORSILD, A. E.   1958.   Geographical distribution of some elements in the flora of Canada. Geograph. Bull. *11*: 57–77.
26. RAUP, H. M.   1947.   The botany of southwestern Mackenzie. Sargentia *6*: 1–275.
27. RITCHIE, J. C.   1964.   Contributions to the Holocene paleoecology of west-central Canada: I, The Riding Mountain area. Can. J. Botany *42*: 181–196.
28. RITCHIE, J. C. and B. de VRIES.   1964.   Contributions to the Holocene paleoecology of west-central Canada: A late-glacial deposit from the Missouri Coteau. Can. J. Botany *42*: 677–692.
29. RITCHIE, J. C., and S. LICHTI-FEDEROVICH.   1963.   Contemporary pollen spectra in central Canada: I, Atmospheric samples at Winnipeg, Manitoba. Pollen et Spores *5*: 95–114.
30. —— 1965.   An early postglacial pollen spectrum from the Missouri Coteau, Saskatchewan (unpublished manuscript).
31. SANGSTER, A. G., and H. M. DALE.   1961.   A preliminary study of differential pollen grain preservation. Can. J. Botany *39*: 35–43.
32. TERASMAE, J.   1961.   Notes on late-Quaternary climatic changes in Canada. Ann. N.Y. Acad. *95*: 658–675.
33. —— Pollen diagram of Scrimbit Farm, Saskatchewan (unpublished diagram).
34. TUTHILL, S. J., L. CLAYTON, and W. M. LAIRD.   1964.   A comparison of a fossil Pleistocene Molluscan fauna from North Dakota with a recent Molluscan fauna from Minnesota. Am. Midl. Nat. *71*: 344–362.
35. VRIES, B. DE.   1964.   An Investigation of a Late-Glacial Deposit from the Missouri Coteau of Saskatchewan. M.Sc. thesis, Univ. Manitoba.
36. WARKENTIN, J.   1964.   The Western Interior of Canada. McClelland & Stewart. 304 pp.
37. WEST, R. G.   1961.   Late-glacial and postglacial vegetational history in Wisconsin, particularly changes associated with the Valders readvance Am. J. Sci. *259*: 766–783.
38. WRIGHT, H. E., JR.   1964a.   Aspects of the early postglacial forest succession in the Great Lakes region. Ecology *45*: 439–448.
39. —— 1964b.   Classification of the Wisconsin glacial stage. J. Geol. *72*: 628–637.
40. WRIGHT, H. E. JR., T. C. WINTER, and H. L. PATTEN.   1963.   Two pollen diagrams from southeastern Minnesota: Problems in the regional late-glacial and post-glacial vegetational history. Bull. Geol. Soc. Am. *74*: 1371–1396.
41. ZOLTAI, S. C.   1961.   Glacial history of part of northwestern Ontario. Proc. Geol. Assoc. Can. *13*: 61–83.
42. —— 1963.   Glacial features of the Canadian Lakehead area. Can. Geograph. *7*: 101–115.

JACQUES ROUSSEAU

Movement of Plants under the Influence of Man

SCIENTISTS WERE NOT THE PROMOTERS of biology during its infancy. It emerged slowly from the store of popular beliefs and the laws governing living organisms were only gradually discovered. Even a major biological science like genetics only abandoned the folkloric world as recently as a century ago.

The plant and animal kingdoms are separated popularly by the idea of motion—movement of animals, fixity of plants—a characteristic believed so fundamental that early scientists catalogued sponges and corals as plants. In this context motion is considered only in the narrow sense of locomotion. Motion was not at first recognized as a fundamental property of any living organism. The evidence was hidden by the slowness of the process. Only after astute observation, do we discover that myxomycetes are creeping. A good span of human life is necessary to realize that a fern with a horizontal rhizome has advanced a little, having produced a new apical bud every year while the older extremity decays. More often, each generation of plants is fixed on a spot and only by seeds are the progeny projected a little farther. The idea that plant communities travel and that man is a factor in the process, supposes the use of a historical scale.

The whole living world behaves like a single colonial organism whose main function is to exist. It is a single mass of protoplasm with multiple facets apparently divided in unrelated fragments but linked by invisible bridges. Continuous growth by multiplying cells is a lethal process. For a number of years, Alexis Carrel grew a piece of chick embryo on a synthetic medium. This cancer-like organism, when it reached a certain size, would have automatically condemned itself to death if trimming had not reduced the mass to a smaller volume. This pruning conferred a relative immortality. Similarly, a geranium in a pot will not grow forever. When cells remote from the apical growth perish, their death presages the end of the whole organism. Fresh cuttings bring a new vigour, and the individual, constantly rejuvenated, grows on indefinitely. In nature, artificial pruning of the chicken embryo or pelargonium finds its equivalent in sex organization. Sexual reproduction is a mere automatic pruning technique. The little fruit fly is nothing more than a fragment of the original protoplasm needing mixing of two individuals at each generation. This very elementary movement favours the perpetual youth of the protoplasm and hence that of the renewed individual. Slight changes, occurring at random, bring to light new species. Senile varieties leave the stage to be replaced by new ones. This obscure movement initiates a rejuvenation of the species and an adaptation to the ever changing environment.

A third type of movement interests us particularly here. In the rather lax, single colonial organism covering the biosphere, the different units struggle one against the other to eliminate the unfit and to try to prevent a cancer-like proliferation. Maintenance of life rests on a malthusian operation, the death of the surplus, the pruning of society. This necessary parade of the living world, in which animals as well as plants participate, tends to renovate the biosphere.

There is a continuous inter-action between the various plants and animals on the earth. Strictly speaking, phytogeography is only an angle of biogeography, and we can define the latter as "The study of spatial inter-action of living organisms and inorganic world." Border lines between scientific disciplines are man-made creations. No discipline is autonomous; all are mere chapters of a common endeavour— the search for the truth.

Action of man on vegetation has not been the same throughout the different ages of humanity. During the gathering and hunting stages, man was a mere species in a balanced association. Geologically speaking, a climax is a degree, a step on the road to evolution. In the span of a few generations, however, the climax appears as a final reality.

The early gatherer did not interfere in nature more than any other species of the association. With development of human culture, his action followed an increasing geometric ratio: he upset the equilibrium in nature, became dominant, and now he governs the biological cover, perfectly ignorant of the future.

In this play, only a part of the action will be shown on the stage, and the actors of this drama will be found in a small collection of plants, mainly weeds and cultivated plants, and, in America, amongst pre-Columbian populations and early European settlers.

MAN AS A FACTOR IN THE ELIMINATION OF SPECIES

Dispersal of plants by man involves both negative and positive movements. Elimination of species, birth of new forms, destruction and building of new biological communities, all these phases, either additive or subtractive, are movements if we consider them from a "demographical" point of view. All these processes will put in action factors governing the migration and establishment of individual species.

During the short span of the two last centuries, a few species of animals were irretrievably lost in Canada. Following the trip of Jacques Cartier, the great auk (*Plautus impennis*) became an important food resource for the European fishermen visiting the Gulf of St. Lawrence. Like the dodo of Mauritius, it is now extinct, the last specimen having been captured in 1870. An eastern variety of the American buffalo (*Bison bison pensylvanicus*), which formerly haunted the Pennsylvania forest, did not resist the white man's invasion. We say sometimes that the eastern woodland wapiti (*Cervus canadensis*) receded to the western part of Canada. The fact is that the eastern subspecies (*C. c. canadensis*) was exterminated and that the species today is represented by two western varieties (*C. c. manitobensis* and *C. c. nelsoni*). Probably the most common bird ever found in Canada was the passenger pigeon (*Ectopistes migratorius*). After 1878, it became rarer each year until the last living specimen finished its days in captivity in an American zoo at the beginning of the present century. Man alone is responsible for extinction of the eastern buffalo and wapiti, but the ravages of hunting will not explain the disappearance of the passenger pigeon. Epidemics might have been a factor. The drastic reduction of the caribou herds (*Rangifer arcticus caboti*) in the Quebec-Labrador peninsula seems to have followed the same pattern. These animal species are being mentioned for example only. I do not intend to list all the factors involved.

When reviewing the flora of eastern Canada in the light of old fragmentary lists—those of discoverers and travelers such as Jacques Cartier, Champlain, Lescarbot, Sagard, Pierre Boucher (18), the Jesuits, and botanists like Jacques Cornut, Michel Sarrazin, Jean-François Gaultier, Pehr Kalm, and André Michaux—we cannot uncover a single species that has become extinct since the establishment of New France. In the northeastern United States, we might mention *Franklinia alatahama*, an attractive flowering endemic shrub. Excessive gathering for decorative purposes was fatal and this species has disappeared like the great auk and the Mauritius dodo.

No other species of plants, as far as I know, has had the same fate in northeastern America. The case of *Mitella prostrata* is sometimes mentioned. This rare endemic, discovered by André Michaux on Lake Champlain in 1792, has been found only once since. It is, in all probability, a mutant of *Mitella diphylla*. Mutation is not unfrequent in nature, but usually mutants disappear within a generation without perpetuating themselves. On my own property in the Quebec bush I found a variegated form and also a screw-leaved variety of balsam fir (*Abies balsamea*). We may wonder if, without protection, more aggressive plants would not eliminate these trees.

Endemics are evidently more menaced than well-distributed species. *Erigeron Provancheri* (10) has been found in only one locality, a narrow cornice ten feet long by one foot wide in the St. Lawrence estuary. On its original site, for unknown reasons, the plant does not expand; in a botanical garden it has become a weed. So-called senility, surely, is not a factor here. A mere alteration of the river bank would eliminate this species—a fate that could well have met many unknown endemics.

We know, nevertheless, that one species in eastern Canada came close to extinction. The rage for ginseng (*Panax quinquefolium*) gathering started in 1716 when Father Lafitau discovered its likeness to an Asiatic species, well known for its overall medicinal properties. The Chinese regarded the plant as a panacea and valued it like gold. Abenaki, Iroquois, and white settlers screened the bush with such efficiency that a fairly common plant was nearly eradicated.

In contrast, other species were protected by primitive taboos or for other reasons. African slaves transported to the West Indies kept major remnants of their old animist and fetichist religion which they blended with the Christian faith to produce a syncretic religion:

voodoo. "Baobab" had a place in original African rites and so was protected. Since it was absent in the New World, another tree was adopted instead, "mapou" (*Ceiba peltandra*), and for that reason was protected in Haiti as baobab was in Africa. Similarly, we are told that *Ginkgo biloba* would probably have disappeared from Asia had it not been protected in the vicinity of temples.

For other reasons, white elm was kept as an integrated member of the newly substituted plant community in the alluvial plain of St. Lawrence Valley. Always scattered in its distribution, this tree was left in the middle of fields cleared from the original forest because its high leafy head produced a shadow travelling with the sun, to the advantage of both pasture growth and cattle needing protection against sunshine.

BIRTH OF NEW HEREDITARY FORMS

Linnaeus described a new veronica from migrant America specimens found near Uppsala, thence its name, "the travelling veronica," *Veronica peregrina*. After expanding in Europe, perhaps it came back to its homeland as a weed. It has always behaved as a weed in eastern Canada, usually growing on tilled ground. Except for occasional river banks, there are hardly any primitive habitats suitable for it. The midwest flora contains a native variety, *Veronica peregrina* var. *xalapensis*. In the last decade, a clear-cut variety, a depressed, half-succulent plant, *V. peregrina* var. *laurentiana* (10), was found in the St. Lawrence estuary. Contrary to the type—if we understand the type from the nomenclatorial, not the biological point of view—it is not a weed. More probably, the plant described by Linnaeus is only a mutant of one or another of the North American wild varieties.

Weeds are usually mutants adapted to tilled soil or growing, like *Polygonum achoreum*, on trodden paths or other artificial habitats. Without even being aware of his responsibility, man introduces them everywhere he goes, far from their original ground, as if they were attached to his feet.

Only cultivated plants contribute to a change of the plant scenery more than weeds. These plants are also mutants, but they are chosen deliberately; they need man's protection and are saved by his constant and vigilant cultivation. Often their wild ancestors are unknown. Common tobacco (*Nicotiana tabacum*) is likely a hybrid of two other species. Maize (*Zea Mays*) does not grow wild, except where it escaped from cultivation. We are not certain of the ancestor of Jerusalem artichoke (*Helianthus tuberosus*).

One explanation of the disappearance of "mother types" can be found in man's interference with nature (11). When a wild mutant appealed to primitive agriculturists it was brought into cultivation and carefully nurtured, while its ancestors were left to fend for themselves in the wild. The area of the cultivated plant may be wider than that of the past, and while the cultivar is well protected in marginal spots there is no chance for the wild variety to survive. Sometimes the species can resist normal parasites, but when the area of cultivation is increased, new pests are transferred to it and become more aggressive. Colorado beetle is said to have adopted the potato only when its cultivation reached the area of the insect.

Before the advent of genetics, cultivated mutants were already numerous. Some were discarded from the market by changing fashions. The Montreal melon was extensively grown until thirty years ago. After the last war, the Micmac Indians of Restigouche were still growing a dwarf maize (*Zea mays*). Both varieties have since disappeared from gardens. After a long search, I found some seeds; they are now being grown in the Montreal Botanical Garden and the strains are thus being preserved.

Except for shrubs and trees, cultivated plants are usually annual tropical plants or perennials treated as annuals. For this reason, tomatoes, squashes, and beans will hardly grow by themselves for more than one generation. Those adapted to a temperate zone, like wheat, might escape cultivation, but they would hardly naturalize themselves. These mutants of annual plants, it seems, are not well equipped to resist competition. Amongst the perennials, hop (*Humulus lupulus*) was already naturalized before 1664, according to Pierre Boucher (1).

New varieties selected by man are used to establish extensive artificial associations. They modify the appearance of the landscape but they usually need constant help to remain a permanent element. Rarely will they integrate themselves with the spontaneous flora, and hence their disappearance is definitely linked to man.

DESTRUCTION AND CREATION OF BIOLOGICAL COMMUNITIES UNDER
HUMAN PRESSURE

When agriculture started in Eurasia in the Neolithic period, forest clearing had to be done by burning, because proper tools were not available (6, 12). This practice, which became a part of civilization, modified the qualities of the soil in such a way that it would seldom produce the old growth formation if left to itself.

Emperor Bonaparte had a decisive influence on eastern American ecology when he imposed the Baltic blockade. Formerly, French and British traders pretended that Canadian timber did not have the market value of that from northern Europe. The truth is that they preferred to trade with foreigners rather than with administrators of Crown forests who would be inclined to control their profits. The road to the Baltic sea being cut, the survival of the British fleet would have been endangered if our colony had not switched from fur trade to timber. The result: white and red pine started to disappear, original growth formations changed, and the frequency of forest fires increased. Today only scattered remnants of the former virgin forest survive.

In subarctic and hemiarctic zones, removal of plant cover facilitates the melting of the discontinuous permafrost. This often initiates a change in vegetation. Examples can be seen around Fort Chimo airport, where the sandy ground easily adopts visitors, and at the old George River post near tree-line, where the clearing of shrubby vegetation gave birth to a prairie of grasses. Near the northern limits of the forest, a bush fire often produces a new tundra patch that does not revert to the original black spruce growth. I have seen such cases in the Quebec–Labrador peninsula and these are becoming more common with the inroads of man.

Near Lake Ouareau, one hundred miles north of Montreal, funnel-shaped holes may be seen. It seems that they were the sites of former permafrost nodules which melted after forest clearing. These pseudo-karstic holes, filled with snow during winter blizzards, support a delayed growth and constitute a new micro-habitat.

A vast portion of the habitat was changed with the breaking of the prairie cover. Only fragments of the original vegetation remained as a reminder of the original flora. Insect fauna probably followed a similar pattern, but mammals, needing a much bigger undisturbed area, started to recede. In a region with such a small annual rainfall, the early intricated mat of vegetation was replaced by a loose stand of annual grasses and erosion soon created deserts, such as the arid zone of southern Saskatchewan, the Iowa dust bowl, and the eroded mountains of China and Haiti.

Man created deserts, but he also created oases. Sahara oases, with date palms growing in sandy bowls near water holes, were usually man-made and were protected for generations by caravan leaders. I saw deserts thirty years ago near Phoenix and Chandler, Arizona, which since, with proper irrigation, have become orchards producing citrus and other fruits.

Some slopes near Fort Chimo are covered with nearly pure stands of tamarack (*Larix laricina*). This species prefers low, moist grounds. Seen from a plane, they are usually rows bordering lakes and rivers. Local habits easily explain the Fort Chimo stand. The post was established in the beginning of the last century, nearly at the limit of arctic tundra and hemiarctic forest tundra. Hudson's Bay Company employees in the eastern arctic heated their houses with wood carried from the south. When felling trees, the Eskimos systematically avoided larches because they were too heavy—a result of their high water content. Spruce disappeared locally, whereas larch remained and reproduced itself, finding a suitable habitat on slopes whose superficial drainage was caused by the impermeability of permafrost and gneisses outcrops.

In Lake Mistassini a dome shaped island is covered with a nearly pure stand of paper birch (*Betula papyrifera*). With its scattered trees and scarce undergrowth, one gets the impression that it is a park. Forest fires are not responsible for the growth pattern. The lake was a favourite fishing spot for the bush Indians who stopped there before taking up their winter quarters. Every year, after blueberry picking and bear hunting, they set their nets there to accumulate a stock of smoked fish for the fall and to wait for snow. Camp fires were maintained whole days, not for cooking purposes, but to dry and smoke fish. It happens also that the Montagnais–Naskapi Indians used only conifers for their fires, avoiding hard wood. Balsam fir and black spruce disappeared and an equilibrium of the second growth forest was artificially maintained.

Other species of birches grow at the forest limit in Lapland. For countless generations, Laps have bred reindeer herds there. In contrast to the paper birches, the distribution of the northern birch species in northern Scandinavia and Iceland coincides with the treeline. From these observations and from their studies of Iceland's vegetation, the Löves (8) have concluded that the island is part of the hemiarctic zone. Where reindeers are bred, birch formations have an orchard-like physiognomy, a consequence of centuries of overgrazing.

North American agriculture began on the arid southern plateaux of Mexico, New Mexico, and Arizona, wanting only a crude system of irrigation to become fertile. This agriculture, as far as the choice of plants is concerned, has nothing in common with the European one. As new mutants were found to be adaptable to a shorter growing season and longer daylight, cultivated fields moved north. The Iroquois, living then in a southern area, received in their turn the string bean (*Phaseolus vulgaris*), the maize plant (*Zea mays*), a pumpkin (*Cucurbita pepo*), and a yellow-flowered tobacco (*Nicotiana rustica*). Since these plants had strains adapted to northern regions, these agriculturists became aggressive and looked north for vital space, finally dislodging the peaceful Algonkian tribes from the St. Lawrence Valley. Forest clearing was done by burning and the soil never amended, except for nitrogen fixation by bean roots. Twenty or thirty years of such cultivation impoverished the soil in such a way that the whole village had to migrate elsewhere. Before Iroquoian occupation, primitive hunters were part of a balanced, ecological formation and never upset nature's equilibrium. As edaphic conditions changed, the irreversibly modified habitat started to produce extensive hawthorn (*Crataegus*) groves. Formerly, hawthorn was maintained only in its native habitats along river banks. These new stands became more or less permanent "maquis," inducing mutant production and facilitating conservation and cross-breeding of new forms. The Iroquois created the *Crataegus* problem (15, 16, 17).

The first European settlers in America brought with them their own European agriculture, hardly borrowing anything from the Amerindian one (15, 16). They tried to copy their homeland ecology, in Quebec, the *bocage normand* and in Acadia, the *marais poitevin*, which was nothing more than polders protected against the sea by *aboiteaux* (dykes). Furthermore, this was done in a climate that was not a counterpart of the European model which included occasional fig and palm trees. The agriculture of New France always remained a gamble—a bet against nature—until new strains of cereals and vegetables were introduced.

Agriculture without scientific help is, at best, a risky enterprise. Under such circumstances, bad years visit more often than one would wish. After Confederation, a perennial disaster persisted for a while in southern Quebec. One after the other, farms were abandoned, houses closed, and their occupants left for New England to find a living in factories. Why didn't these farmers migrate to the newly opened western Prairies? The answer to this question lies in the fact that until recent times it cost much more for an immigrant to travel from eastern Canada to the Prairies than from Europe to the Prairies.

The deficiency of plant cover and the lack of government vision resulted in a loss of two million inhabitants to Canada. The abandoned farms were quickly visited by wild red cherry (*Prunus pensylvanica*), old field birch (*Betula populifolia*), aspen (*Populus tremuloides*), and other poplars (mainly *P. grandidentata* and *P. Jackii*), plants which were adapted to these second growth formations. Conifers came back later, but the habitat never fully returned to its former climax. Ecological conditions had been upset for centuries.

In the West Indies, a deep growth of sugar cane replaced the original native vegetation. In the southern United States, cotton became the staple product. Since the white man is not too anxious or able to do hard work in warm countries, such an agriculture required a supply of cheap labour, and for that purpose slaves were bought on the African market like cattle. Eventually, slavery was officially abolished, but its socio-economic status was maintained by wages kept low in order to produce crops at minimum cost and to enable idle owners to receive dividends. Today, agriculture is a business, producing revenues for other persons than those actually engaged in its working operations. The whole agitation in the world below the fortieth parallel is nothing more than a response to ecological factors (in human as well as plant life), a search for equilibrium, a wish to adjust the unbalanced conditions created by the movement of plants under the white man's guidance.

When passing from the primitive gathering stage to the more sophisticated stage of agriculture, humanity started an assault on nature designed to upset its equilibrium. This was a vital necessity. Extension of cultivated areas supplied more food, for which there was a great need, and allowed greater numbers of offspring to survive. Starvation receded somewhat. Infanticide was no more a vital necessity for all those who wanted to survive. Whenever plant cover was replaced somewhere by a crop-producing one, economic and social implications were involved.

According to one report (5), 22 per cent of the native Finland flora has lost territory on account of cultivation; but at the same time about 42 per cent of the species have become more common. No attempt was ever made to evaluate such a change in Canada.

The forests of Europe have been humanized for countless generations. I am most familiar with the French one. In the French forest, original herbaceous and shrubby cover has nearly disappeared and is partly replaced by a kind of lawn admitting so many well-adapted, introduced plants that one would think them native. To a Canadian, these forests look like parks. Even the tree community differs from the original one. Those of economic importance are protected until they will give an optimum crop, thus producing what are really cultivated forests.

Artificial clearings facilitate spontaneous naturalization of aggressive, monospecific formations. The large-flowered evening primrose (*Oenothera Lamarckiana*), although of American origin, apparently does not grow wild in America, but it has found a proper habitat on Holland wharfs, dykes, and railroad yards. *Elodea canadensis* sometimes interrupt navigation in the canals of Holland and France. *Erigeron canadense*, which is seldom seen in extensive pure stands in eastern Canada, has become an aggressive weed in Europe. On the other hand, *Hieracium aurantiacum*—a rarity of the Alps, where botanists show it in alpine botanical gardens—gives a uniform orange color to Laurentian fields. The St. Lawrence River has a water line covered with purple loosetrife (*Lythrum Salicaria*) and flowering rush (*Butomus umbellatus*). Although both were introduced, they now seem to be in equilibrium as if they were in their own native habitat. Are the cockleburs (*Xanthium*) indigenous to these shores? They are so much at ease on the banks of the St. Lawrence that we cannot distinguish which is native and which is not. Without these species, our shores would have a completely different physiognomy.

A few decades ago the city of Montreal received the visit of an invader from South America—*Galinsoga parviflora*. The plants behaved like squatters and rapidly became Canadian citizens. These are now amongst the most conspicuous plants to be found in Montreal, along with the ragweeds (*Ambrosia trifida* and *A. artemisiifolia*) and *Iva xanthifolia*, which travelled from the central and western United States.

Introduced plants do not all establish themselves definitively. Corn poppy (*Papaver Rhoeas*) tried without success for decades, but did not naturalize itself because its seeds started to germinate in late summer and were killed by frost. The alcoholic ferment does not acclimatize itself perfectly in our country. It was introduced in Canada for brewing purposes, but it is generally necessary to sow spores every time we need them; otherwise the acetic ferment would dominate and produce vinegar. Wine producers in France usually rely on surrounding native ferments. Pre-Columbian America had alcoholic beverages in Mexico and parts of the southern United States, but not in Canada. Climatic factors might be involved. It may also be that the sugar content of our fruits is not high enough. Socio-cultural reasons and tradition, perhaps, are alone responsible in that particular case, but ecological factors may also be involved.

MOVEMENTS OF INDIVIDUAL PLANTS

The fact that man is a major factor in the movement of plants does not need supplementary examples to be established. But the question of his exact importance remains to be determined. All cases are not alike. Some species were deliberately acclimatized by early man; in other cases acclimatization was spontaneous, although nonetheless indirectly induced by man. Lack of documentation often restricts us to hypotheses, and there is always a great temptation to choose those we like without giving enough weight to alternate suggestions. As long as there is an opening for alternate possibilities, a process or a fact is not demonstrated. This is self-evident, but basic principles are sometimes forgotten. The following examples will show a few different ways in which plants have become acclimatized.

Pre-Columbian introductions from Asia. As far as we know, not a single cultivated Asiatic plant was introduced in America in pre-Columbian times. Only a domestic animal, the dog, accompanied man. Amerindian and Asiatic agricultures developed independently with mongolic migrations to America which began before the discovery of agriculture in Neolithic Eurasia. The first known immigrants were gatherers and hunters, and it was only when the American hordes reached the central American plateau that agriculture became established on our continent.

Thuja occidentalis in France. When Jacques Cartier wintered near Quebec in 1535–36, an "epidemic" of scurvy decimated his crew. He made a promise to visit the sanctuary of Roc-Amadour, in France, as a pilgrim, if his men were restored to health. Soon afterwards he met a Stadacone Indian who had been in France with him the previous year, and who indicated that *arbor vitae* (*Thuja occidentalis*) was the local specific remedy for that illness. An infusion of these high vitamin content leaves acted miraculously and the whole crew was immediately cured. Four centuries later, I went to Roc-Amadour and saw many small *arbor vitae* on the straight cliffs. The species had made the pilgrimage to the sanctuary. It is normal to conclude, and this would satisfy a romantic spirit, that Cartier not only made the promised pilgrimage, but also introduced the miraculous cure at the sanctuary. Unfortunately there is no written statement that such a thing happened, but we know for certain that *arbor vitae* and white pine (*Pinus Strobus*) were introduced by him and that some were given to the king's garden in France (13, 14). From there to Roc-Amadour, birds might have been a factor in the dissemination. The old French forester Philibert Guinier considered them an important disseminator of that species.

Lagenaria siceraria. According to the ethnologist Nordenskiold, the occurrence of the calabash in America and Polynesia in pre-Columbian times would be the best proof of pre-historic contacts between those distant regions. It was assumed that a calabash floating on ocean water would soon lose its vitality. Nevertheless, Whitaker and Carter (19), looking for a clear demonstration, have reported that:

Under conditions simulating ocean drift, gourds of *Lagenaria siceraria* were found to be capable of floating for periods up to 224 days with no significant decrease in viability of the seed. From what is known of the velocities of oceanic currents, this length of time would be sufficient for gourds to drift from tropical Africa to the coast of Brazil by the South Atlantic Current. Up to 95 days immersion in sea water did not impair viability of the seeds as compared with dry controls. This would indicate that the critical factor in the distribution of this species by oceanic drift is the ability of the gourd to float.

Camp (2) also commented on the source of the American pre-Columbian gourd:

While there is a possibility that it may have been carried from Africa to the shores of South America by ocean currents, there is no evidence that this gourd is a littoral plant. The chance of its establishment after accidental introduction by flotation, therefore, is an exceedingly remote one. This gourd has long been used by peoples of southeastern Asia, both for food and for the making of utensils of various sorts, and it seems more likely to have been introduced by early migrants from Asia to America. The resistance of its seeds to salt water would make it an admirable subject for introduction where an open, spray-drenched craft only were available.

The conclusions proposed by Camp are too drastic. Even if there is only "one remote chance of introduction by flotation," the hypothesis has to be considered. High frequency of a possibility does not render it the only choice.

The same explanation could apply to Trans-Atlantic drifts. Spontaneous migration from one continent to another would be sufficient to explain distributional disjunctions. Cases of disjunction of area are innumerable. *Scirpus alpinus* is found in isolated spots of Anticosti and in the Alps. We cannot see now how man's activity would be a factor in this disrupted distribution. However, in the case of the gourd, we can understand that anywhere a primitive population finds such a plant, the use of the gourd is obvious, even if such a trait was not in the primitive population's tradition.

Cocos nucifera. According to a Cingalese proverb, coconut will grow only where it hears the noise of waves and man. Current opinion is that coconuts will thrive only when sown by man and do not tolerate transportation by ocean drift. This assumption needs actual confirmation. It would be sufficient to prove that one fruit out of ten thousand is carried by ocean drift without loss of viability to establish that ocean drift might be possible, particularly on low beaches where an unusual wave, inflated by wind velocity, might place the seed above the high water level.

Juglans nigra, Malus ioensis, Shepherdia argentea. According to Gilmore (4), isolated colonies of these plants growing together outside their general areas indicate former Amerindian cultures. Nevertheless, we cannot eliminate other possibilities. Squirrels might carry walnuts, birds the other seeds. A former, more extended area might also have been disrupted by numerous causes. But if the general area of each of the above mentioned species does not coincide, and if the association of these species in isolated colonies is frequent, then the Amerindian hypothesis acquires a higher degree of reliability.

Podophyllum peltatum and *Elaeagnus argentea* (Quebec). May apple (*Podophyllum peltatum*) bears an edible fruit often used by primitive Indians. Furthermore, its root was the regular poison employed for suicides, a rather common event. Quebec province is presently outside its general area. Plants are found on Mount Royal, where there was once an Iroquoian *bourgade* and at Pierreville, where Abenaki Indians have a reservation. On the other hand, the silver-leaved plant, *Elaeagnus argentea*, whose berries were eaten by Amerindian natives, is found in Quebec entirely outside its general range—on Lake Temiskaming, at the western extremity of Orleans island, on an open part of Bic Island, and on Mont Saint-Pierre, Gaspé peninsula —all of which were known as camping sites for Indians. At Mont Saint-Pierre, the plant is now found at the summit of the cliff, where ecological conditions are more favourable, whereas the Indian camping places were in the valley bottom a few hundred feet away. It is reasonable to believe that Indians were a factor in the migration of these species, but the other processes described in preceding paragraphs have also to be considered. W. G. Dore (personal communication) has found other localities for May apple, all linked with Indian camping places. In a paper under preparation, he also mentions other Amerindian economic plants found outside their range in the vicinity of Ottawa on the old portage between the St. Lawrence and Ottawa rivers. Like the examples quoted in the above paragraph, accumulation of various data increases the reliability of the hypothesis.

DELIBERATE INTRODUCTION OF USEFUL PLANTS AND CHANCE INTRODUCTION
OF WEEDS INTO THE PROVINCE OF QUEBEC

Many economic and weedy plants introduced into Quebec during its early settlement have become naturalized. The cultivated asparagus (*Asparagus officinalis*) and parsnip (*Pastinaca sativa*) were mentioned for the first time by Pierre Boucher (1) in 1664; the latter species were grown previously at Port Royal, Acadia in 1612 according to Lescarbot (7). Both plants are well acclimatized on the low islands of the St. Lawrence in the district of Montreal and in other habitats. According to Pierre Boucher (1), hop (*Humulus Lupulus*), an early introduction used for brewing purposes, was already a naturalized plant in 1664. Since it is propagated mainly by root stocks it most likely escaped from gardens. Garden sorrel (*Rumex acetosa*), always a popular vegetable in France, was grown at Quebec in Champlain's time in 1618 and is also mentioned by Boucher (1). It seems to have escaped from gardens, but its introduction as a weed is not completely to be discarded. The fact that its acclimatization is very limited in the province of Quebec and that it grows mainly near Quebec city (according to Marie-Victorin, 9) would rather suggest the first hypothesis. Hemp (*Cannabis sativa*) was grown at Port Royal from 1606 to 1608. Its cultivation in Quebec, mentioned for the first time in 1664 by Pierre Boucher (1), remained unimportant until Intendant Talon ordered its extension in 1667. It is no longer grown, and is still a prohibited crop, but it is found as a weed. Timothy grass (*Phleum pratense*) was brought to the United States in 1746 and its cultivation was strongly advocated by a certain Timothy Hanson of Baltimore, hence its name. Extensively grown in Quebec as hay, its presence in bush clearings is usually an indication of the use of horses for winter lumbering purposes.

Perinwinkle (*Vinca minor*), because of its habitat, seems to have escaped from cultivation. At one time it was frequently used as a medicinal plant. Box elder (*Acer Negundo*), growing wild in Canada near Winnipeg, was introduced early into New France and from there into France by Governor LaGalissoniere around 1755. In Quebec, it became naturalized like white poplar (*Populus alba*) and common willow (*Salix alba*) and has been grown there from an unknown date. Of the flowering shrubs that escaped cultivation and were naturalized in our flora, only roses are mentioned by Pierre Boucher (1). *Rosa rugosa* and *Rosa cinnamomea*, surely escaped cultivation. Sweetbriar (*Rosa Eglanteria*), also introduced, was a medicinal plant which has been in use since medieval times. I do not know if it was grown for that purpose; perhaps it was used as stock for graft roses. Lilac (*Syringa vulgaris*), introduced into cultivation in eastern Canada at an early date escaped from gardens, as did spurge laurel (*Daphne Mezereum*), day-lily (*Hemerocallis fulva*), saffron lily (*Lilium croceum*), and life-forever (*Sedum purpureum*). However, these plants never became important elements of our local flora. When I prepared the chapter on violets for the *Flore laurentienne* (9), I did not mention the fragrant violet (*Viola odorata*), but a few years later I found it perfectly at ease in the Beloeil mountain forest.

Even if we find a date for the first cultivation of horse-radish (*Armoracia rusticana*), water cress (*Nasturtium Nasturtium-aquaticum*), caraway (*Carum carvi*), tansy, chicory, and purslane, this will not be an indication they escaped cultivation, since they were already weeds in Europe and it is perhaps in that capacity that they first travelled here. Common tansy (*Tanacetum vulgare*), once a necessary condiment of Yorkshire pudding was never, as far as I am aware, a French condiment but it had always been a popular medicinal plant. It is commonly found in Quebec as a weed near old settlements and this might suggest that it escaped from gardens. According to Pierre Boucher (1), chicory was grown in 1664, but we do not know if it was *Cichorium Endivia* or *C. Intybus*, the latter species being a widely acclimatized weed. Purslane (*Portulaca oleracea*), according to the same author, was already a member of the spontaneous flora of New France when cultivation of the improved variety was common in France. Previously (1618), Champlain and Sagard saw purslane invading Huron gardens and, possibly under the influence of French missionaries, being used in their sagamite. Daisy (*Chrysanthemum leucanthemum*) is one of the most common weeds of our country. Nevertheless, its invasion in certain districts is rather slow. At Lake Ouareau, one hundred miles north of Montreal, the fields east of the lake were literally invaded by this plant, but there was not a single plant on the western side where the numerous summer residences could only be reached by boat. Ten years after the development started, a road was built to circle the lake, and immediately the daisy appeared on the western side.

Buttercup (*Ranunculus acris*) is also an old introduced weed, although we do not know when its migration occurred. Common everywhere in uninhabited places, it is also found in lumber clearings and along rarely travelled forest roads as well. Weeds are always uncommon far from roads. Only a few are to be found at Lake Mistassini, where, until today, contact was only by plane and canoe. When I surveyed the region between 1944 and 1948, not a single weed was found on the various portages except on the portage between Lake Albanel and Lake Mistassini along the discharge. There, at both extremities of the portage, were found well-established colonies of buttercup. This portage is an old one and was visited by Louis Jolliet as early as 1679. A French trading-post had even been built at that time near its outlet. At another post built by the same Louis Jolliet at Rivière à l'Huile, on Anticosti Island, I also found the buttercup.

Dandelion (*Taraxacum officinale*) and common plantain (*Plantago major*) were among the first weeds carried by the white man. For that reason, early Indians called plantain "the white man's foot." These two common plants are found everywhere in eastern Canada. We should not conclude, however, that they are always introduced weeds because there is a possibility that we have native ecotypes of these species around the Gulf of St. Lawrence.

DATE OF WEED INTRODUCTIONS

Weeds started to invade Canada during the first influx of European settlers. Indians had noticed the coming of the plantain. Champlain and Sagard had seen purslane in the Huron country, about 1618, a few years after the white man visited the region. In 1700, Michel Sarrazin collected *Rorippa amphibia*, a plant that was already well established. Pierre Boucher (1) placed amongst native plants, purslane, hop, and *Melilotus*, but since he wrote only "mélilot," I do not know if it is *Melilotus alba* or *M. officinalis*. Fernald (3) saw "Jesuits' influences" in the introduction of four common weeds: *Silene Cucubalus*, *Artemisia vulgaris*, *Sonchus arvensis*, and *Hieracium vulgatum*. Let us recognize that these introductions are imputable to the white man, particularly the Frenchmen, because the region of the introductions was under French colonial influence.

SPONTANEOUS TRANSPORTATION OF LOCAL PLANTS BY EARLY MAN

Forest-clearing for agricultural purposes and road-building created an excellent environment for indigenous plants adapted to full sunlight. Fire-weed (*Epilobium angustifolium*), which formerly habitated river banks and regions destroyed by forest fires, became a common sight along roads. The narrow margin between fields, cleared but not cultivated, provided an ideal habitat for raspberry (*Rubus idaeus*), strawberry (*Fragaria virginiana*), red-osier dogwood (*Cornus stolonifera*), and many species which now enjoy the widest distribution in eastern Canada. Cow parsnip (*Heracleum lanatum*) and white American hellebore (*Veratrum viride*), also found in such habitats, are native plants of subalpine or subarctic, open habitats.

EPIDEMICS

The following algal epidemics can not be attributed to early man, but since they represent a chapter not yet covered it would seem advisable to mention them. A few years ago, *Cladaphora crispata* started to block the waterworks intake in the Montreal district in early June. The plant, which had an unusual growth, was in its floating stage. Meteorological factors were involved, but the exceptional growth was due to the high content of fertilizers poured in the river sewage system. A chain diatom, a *Melosira*, also once became so abundant that it blocked filters of Montreal waterworks in winter. Water pollution, caused by man, created both these epidemic algal growths.

CONCLUSION

Except for epidemics, the most common elements of the flora seem to be static; nevertheless, landscape design and style are changing. There is a continuous movement, but it is often inconspicuous. When an object moves, our eye registers a succession of images and transmits them to the brain. We claim to have seen a movement, but we have had only a series of individual pictures. With surrounding flora, the succession of new images is also such a slow motion that we are unable to resolve the movement in our brain.

Human society during the span of a generation also remains apparently unchanged. Nevertheless, like a plant society, it constantly evolves and with a speed the eye does not evaluate; that imperceptible movement, another tool, history, will register. Everything alive, any member of the biosphere has movement. Every species and every society represent a column of pilgrims not only travelling in space, but also in time.

REFERENCES

1. BOUCHER, P. 1664. Histoire véritable et naturelle des mœurs et productions du pays de la Nouvelle-France, vulgairement dite le Canada. Paris. 168 pp.
2. CAMP, W. H. 1954. A possible source for American pre-Columbian gourds. Am. J. Botany *41*: 700–701.
3. FERNALD, M. L. 1900. Some Jesuit influences upon our northeastern flora. Rhodora 2: 133–142.

4. GILMORE, M. R. 1930. Dispersal by Indians: a factor in the extension of discontinuous distribution of certain species of native plants. Mich. Acad. Sci. Arts. Letters: vol. 13.

5. KALLIOLA, R. 1961. Man's influence on nature in Finland. Fennia 86: 9–23.

6. KUHNHOLTZ-LORDAT, G. 1938. La terre incendiée. Essai d'agronomie comparée. Maison Carrée, Nîmes, France. 361 pp.

7. LESCARBOT, M. 1612. Relation dernière de ce qui s'est passé au voyage du sieur de Poutrincourt en La Nouvelle-France depuis 20 mois ença. Paris. Reproduced in Thwaites ed., Jesuit Relations 2: 121–191. The English translation on page 165 renders Naveaux as parsnip, and panais as turnip, whereas, in fact, naveaux should be translated as turnip and panais as parsnip.

8. LÖVE, A., and D. LÖVE. 1956. Cytotaxonomical conspectus of the Icelandic flora. Acta Horti Gotoburgensis 20: 65–290.

9. MARIE-VICTORIN, Fr. 1935. Flore laurentienne. Les Frères des Ecoles Chrétiennes, Montréal. 917 pp.

10. MARIE-VICTORIN, Fr., and J. ROUSSEAU. 1940. Nouvelles entités de la flore phanérogamique du Canada oriental. Contr. Inst. Bot. Univ. Montréal 36: 1–74.

11. ROUSSEAU, J. 1938. Pourquoi les ancêtres de certaines plantes cultivées sont disparus ? Ann. ACFAS 4: 113.

12. ―――― 1944. L'aurore de l'agriculture. L'Actualité Econ. 2: 344–361.

13. ―――― 1953. The annedda mystery, 117–129. In XIX Congrès international de Physiologie. Montréal, Canada.

14. ―――― 1954. L'annedda et l'arbre de vie. Revue Hist. Am. Fr. 8: 171–212.

15. ―――― 1957. L'Indien de la forêt boréale, élément de la formation écologique. Roy. Soc. Can., Studia Varia 1957: 37–51. Univ. Toronto Press.

16. ―――― 1961. La trame forestière de l'histoire canadienne. Cahiers des Dix 26: 17–54.

17. ―――― 1962–63. La forêt mixte du Québec dans la perspective historique. Cahiers Géogr. Québec 7: 111–120.

18. ―――― 1964. Pierre Boucher, naturaliste et géographe, 262–400. In P. Boucher, Histoire véritable et naturelle des mœurs et production du pays de la Nouvelle-France, vulgairement dite le Canada. Reprint ed. 1964. Société d'histoire de Boucherville, Boucherville, Québec.

19. WHITAKER, T. W., and G. F. CARTER. 1954. Oceanic drift of gourds— experimental observations. Am. Jour. Botany 41: 697–700.

ROBERT K. S. LEE

Development of Marine Benthic Algal Communities on Vancouver Island, British Columbia

THE NATURE OF THE FORM AND STRUCTURE of intertidal algal communities is an aspect of synecology of which we know very little. But just as little attention has been focused and just as little information is available on two related aspects of synecology: one dealing with description and classification (e.g., Muenscher, 12; Dexter, 4; Isaac, 8; Beveridge and Chapman, 1; Molinier, 10); the other dealing with trophic, or energy relationships (e.g., Lindeman, 9; Sargent and Austin, 16; Odum and Odum, 14; Gordon and Kelly, 6). By way of definition, the three aspects may be classified into the categories of community *morphology*, community *taxonomy*, and community *metabolism*.

From the standpoint of the present research, community morphology is largely concerned with the interpretation of the form and structure of communities. As is true with any complex morphological problem, the morphological nature of algal communities can be interpreted best from evidence derived and synthesized from observations made on their developmental aspects. This approach is well expressed, although for a different purpose, by Weaver and Clements (17, p. 104): "The major difficulty in the analysis of vegetation is its great complexity, but it discloses a definite pattern when analyzed from the developmental point of view."

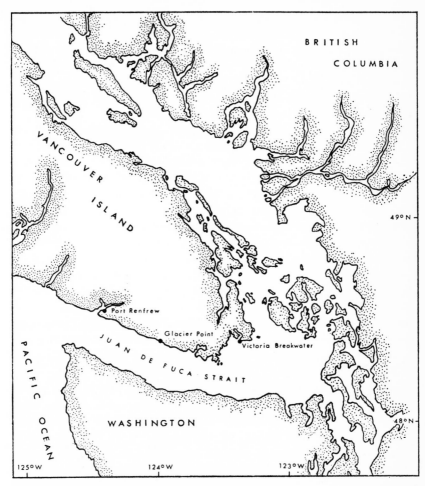

FIGURE 1. Southwest portion of British Columbia, showing the three experimental sites: Port Renfrew, Glacier Point, and Victoria Breakwater.

Accordingly, a developmental study was carried out on three types of intertidal communities between May 1962 and January 1964. Each was in a different area on the southeast part of Vancouver Island on Juan de Fuca Strait (Fig. 1). The community types studied and their locations were: a *Balanus–Fucus* type near the Port Renfrew wharf (Fig. 2), a *Hedophyllum–Corallina–Bossiella* type at Glacier Point (Fig. 3), and an *Alaria–Corallina–Bossiella* type on the breakwater at Victoria Harbor (Figs. 4–8).

Periodic (usually monthly) observations were made on communities developing on denuded rock surfaces and on *in situ* communities. Denuding was done by first removing the larger forms with a penknife, followed by scraping and brushing with a paint scraper and a wire brush, and finally burning with a weed-burner. The burning treatment eliminated the possibility of any living material remaining on the surface and gave a "cleaner" surface than with scraping and brushing alone.

At the Victoria breakwater six denuded plots, each measuring 1.0 to 1.6 m², were initiated at different times of a year. They were situated at about the 0.5 m tide level (by Canadian standards). Each of the other experimental sites had only one denuded plot. At Port Renfrew the plot was 1.6 m² and it ranged from the 1.2 to the 2.1 m tide level. At Glacier Point the plot was 3.5 m² and it was situated from the 0.6 to the 1.5 m tide level. By using the quadrat method, a method familiar to terrestrial plant ecologists, species-distribution indices of frequency and abundance were taken to quantitatively describe the stages of re-colonization. Data relative to the development process, such as life-span and period of reproduction of the species involved, were also gathered.

A detailed account of the results obtained is given in a thesis submitted to the University of British Columbia in partial fulfilment of

---

FIGURES 2–8. (2)Denuded plot at Port Renfrew photographed on 16 June, 1962, 13 days after denuding. The right half of the boulder supports the control community. (3) Denuded plot at Glacier Point photographed on 17 June, 1962, 13 days after denuding. The meter-stick lies on the non-denuded half of the boulder. The *in situ* communities on and adjacent to the boulder served as controls. (4) Portion of the Victoria Harbour breakwater photographed on 5 August, 1963, at low tide. The six denuded plots were on the lowest (6th) tier. The algal growth to the left of the breakwater is *Nereocystis luetkeana*. (5) The *Urospora wormskioldii* and *Entermorpha linza* stage on Victoria Plot I photographed on 20 July, 1962, 60 days after denuding. Some of the algae on the non-denuded block to the left are *Iridaea cordata, Odonthalia floccosa, Microcladia borealis*, and *Bossiella plumosa*. (6) On the right is a portion of the Victoria Plot III colonizing community, composed mainly of *Monostroma fuscum* and *Spongomorpha coalita*. On the left is part of a control colony community with *Alaria marginata, Corallina vancouveriensis*, and *Bossiella plumosa* dominating. Photographed on 5 August, 1963, 164 days after denuding. (7) The block with part of it in the centre of the photograph is Victoria Plot I on 23 May, 1963, 367 days after denuding. It can hardly be distinguished from the non-denuded blocks above and below it. (8) Close-up photograph of boxed section in Fig. 7. It shows a dense patch of *Ulva lobata* and *Enteromorpha linza* occupying an area on the denuded plot (bottom half of the photograph) which, at the time, had only small, young thalli of *Iridaea cordata, Odonthalia floccosa, Corallina vancouveriensis*, and *Bossiella plumosa*.

the requirements for the Ph.D. degree. What follows is (1) a synopsis of the results, presented in accordance with one of the objectives of the study, namely, to determine the pattern of development; and (2) an analysis of the data to provide an explanation for the cause of the pattern.

The pattern of colonization can be determined by examining the frequency percentage figures presented in Tables I–VIII (see group of tables at end of article). The figures were obtained with the aid of a gridded apparatus. This charting device had a 1 × 1 m wooden frame enclosing an area that was divided by wires into 20 × 20 cm grids. By counting the number of grids, or subplots, in which a given species occurred and then converting this number to percentage of occurrence, the frequency percentage of the given species was obtained. The percentages also indicate the seasonal aspect of development, something which could be seen by comparing plots that were denuded at about the same time of a year. For example, Victoria Plots I and IV, which were denuded during May 1962 and June 1963, respectively, are more similar in development than those plots which were denuded at a different time of a year. The same is true for Victoria Plot II, denuded during August 1962, and Victoria Plot V, denuded during August 1963. This can be attributed to the seasonal appearance of certain algae and to the presence of optimum growth periods for those algae which appear throughout most of the year.

Algae that produced new thalli most abundantly (sometimes exclusively) during the colder months of the year included *Navicula grevillei, Ralfsia fungiformis, Costaria costata, Alaria marginata, Antithamnion subulatum,* and *Odonthalia floccosa.* The existence of such populants became noticeable after a preliminary examination of the data gathered from the 1962 denuded plots. The indication then was that the general sequence of events occurring was predictable, but that the sequence could be altered by what appeared to be "winter" populants. To demonstrate this with more reliable experimental evidence, a "winter" plot was established. This was Plot VI at Victoria. The results (Table VI) were drastically different from that of the "non-winter" plots. *Ralfsia fungiformis* was the first populant noticed. It was followed by *Alaria marginata, Prionitis lyallii,* and *Antithamnion subulatum.* They appeared during December and January, within 56 days after denuding. This pattern of development was distinctive; at the other plots the earliest benthic populant was a diatom, after which came certain green algal species.

Amphipleura rutilans, a sessile, colonial diatom, and the green algal species *Urospora mirabilis, Urospora wormskioldii, Enteromorpha linza, Monostroma fuscum* and *Ulva lobata* (see Fig. 5–8) were consistent in appearing on the other plots at Victoria and, with the exception of *Monostroma fuscum*, on the single plot at Glacier Point. Indeed, among these six plots the species displayed a pattern of development that had a high degree of unanimity. The order and time of appearance were as follows: *Amphipleura rutilans*, within 13 days after denuding; *Urospora* spp., within 15 days; *Enteromorpha linza*, within 27 days; *Monostroma fuscum*, within 63 days; *Ulva lobata*, within 118 days. A notable feature of these series of colonizers was that the first was represented by a colonial, unicellular organism, the second by filamentous individuals, and the third by parenchymatous types. Moreover, during these first appearances, the species were usually represented by populations that eventually had such a high density and high frequency percentage that they gave the appearance of pure stands. These gregarious populations were usually composed of individuals representing a wide range of growth stages, from tiny germlings to large, fertile thalli. Because of the presence of an array of growth stages, and because of a short life-span, it would appear that the stand itself was not composed of any one "persisting" group of individuals but rather it was being perpetuated by a continuous series of maturing individuals.

Microtransect experiments revealed that the thalli of these early populants were short-lived. For example, of a total of 18 individuals of *Ulva lobata* plotted on two of the transects at the Victoria breakwater, only seven remained after 11 to 14 days. Of the seven, three showed growth (length) increases of 2.0 to 7.5 cm and four had decreased measurements, apparently due to erosion. The ephemeral character of the green algae can be correlated with the relatively short period of time it takes them to become mature (i.e., fertile). Table IX provides a general representation of the growth and maturation periods for most of the species involved in the study.

Members of the Phaeophyta and Rhodophyta made first appearances during or after the green algal stage. Among the most consistent early arrivals were *Iridaea cordata, Pterosiphonia bipinnata*, and *Polysiphonia hendryi*. These species sometimes appeared before the presence of *Monostroma fuscum* and *Ulva lobata* was noted. In contrast to the diatom and green algal populations, the browns and reds tended to have populations that had relatively low densities and frequency percentages. The low density can be readily attributed to their growth habit. Species such as *Pterosiphonia bipinnata* and *Polysiphonia hen-*

dryi, besides having an erect shoot portion, also had a rather extensive prostrate branching system. In *Pterosiphonia bipinnata* this system was found to be up to 10 cm in diameter at Victoria Plot III. Other species, like *Iridaea cordata, Odonthalia floccosa, Alaria marginata,* and *Costaria costata,* had spreading holdfasts, either disc-like or branching, which precluded the high degree of gregarious growth found in the green algae mentioned above. However, a special type of gregariousness might be noted here in that the disc-like holdfast of *Iridaea cordata* or *Odonthalia floccosa* nearly always had several erect shoots, each at a different stage of development.

A definite order of events in the brown and red algae could not be described because of their sparse growth. In contrast, the presence of each of the early-appearing diatom and green algal species was made evident by a great abundance of individuals, which in effect masked the existence of other species. The indication is that the pattern of development displayed by these early colonizers was, in part, a measure of the *relative conspicuousness* of the species with respect to time. With diatom and green algal species, conspicuousness was due to the combined effect of high density and wide distribution.

With the subsequent growth and maturation of the brown and red algal thalli, the plots gradually took on the appearance of adjacent *in situ* communities (Fig. 7). The time of development, from denudation to the *in situ* condition, was 340 days at Victoria Plot I and 282 days at Victoria Plot II. It is significant to note that the time of year at which both plots appeared like the *in situ* communities was the same—May, 1963. This can be attributed to the favourable growth period at this time of year for the species involved. The *in situ* condition, characterized by *Alaria marginata, Corallina vancouveriensis, Bossiella plumosa,* and to a smaller degree by *Iridaea cordata, Odonthalia floccosa,* and *Petrocelis franciscana,* was also considered to be, in part, a matter of relative conspicuousness. In this case, however, conspicuousness was related more to size than to abundance.

The other plots at Victoria were still in a pre-*in situ* state when the field observations were terminated. At Glacier Point the situation was somewhat different; after 590 days from denuding, the plot supported only six species (Table VII). But during May 1963, or 354 days after denuding, 11 species were present. Perhaps a combination of physical factors, such as the declivity and smooth texture of the rock surface together with vigorous surf action, prevented any prolonged attachment of the thalli. Apparently in such a situation, anchorage can be a major problem.

The Port Renfrew plot, situated high in the intertidal zone, displayed a different type of development, at least in terms of species involved (Table VIII). The first colonizers were *Enteromorpha linza*, *Rhizoclonium riparium*, and *Bangia fuscopurpurea*. The plot, 328 days after denuding, supported an *in situ* type of community which was composed largely of *Fucus evanescens* and *Balanus cariosus*. As shown in Table VIII, there were four species that were removed in denuding but did not reappear as colonizers—even after 499 days. It is perhaps significant that at the time of removal, each of the four species was represented by only one, two, or three individuals.

An interesting developmental aspect of this plot was the relationship between the extensive *Balanus cariosus* population and the algal community. Prior to denuding, the algal community was epizoic on the shells of the barnacle. Young, attached stages of the animal were first noticed 47 days after the plot was denuded. By 263 days after denuding they grew over most of the plot. Most, if not all, of the algal growth was attached to the shells of the barnacle. Prior to this, when the barnacle population was sparsely distributed, most of the algae were saxicolous.

An orderly appearance of colonizing forms on artificially-placed substrates or on denuded rock surfaces has been observed by other workers in various parts of the world (e.g., Wilson, 18; Bokenham, 2; Rees, 15; Northcraft, 13; Molinier and Picard, 11; Cirino, 3; Hartog, 7). The species involved depended for the most part on the locality, both general (geographical) and specific (intertidal position). But although the species may differ, these observations and those of the present study point out an interesting relationship among the succeeding populations or communities. This relationship is a morphological one, whereby short-lived, fast-growing forms are succeeded by long-lived, slow-growing forms. This type of succession was recognized particularly first by Bokenham (2) and later by Northcraft (13), and Fahey and Doty (5). It appears that, from the standpoint of the morphology of the colonizers, the pattern of development presented by different workers shows conformity. Differences lie in attempts to explain why the pattern occurs as it does.

A review of the literature reveals that two schools of thought prevail: one contends that the development process is an expression of ecological succession; the other argues against ecological succession. The distinction, however, may be only arbitrary. This is due to the fact that it is not always clear how the word succession is being used. Succession in the ordinary use of the term implies orderly sequence. As an ecological term, succession must mean a process of community development in which formation of a given stage is dependent on the environmental changes brought on by a previous stage. Obviously the term must be used with definition to avoid ambiguity. But the problem involves more than mere definition. It also involves, more significantly, interpretation, for according to some workers orderly sequence is indicative of ecological succession.

To illustrate this *a priori* approach to interpreting observed data, the work of Cirino (3, p. 31) may be cited. Unlike most other authors, she leaves little doubt as to how she uses the term succession.

> Biotic succession is employed synonymously with seral progression, true succession, succession proper, or seral succession. It is interpreted as indicative of a series of changes in the biota of any community considered as a whole, exclusive of seasonal variations. . . . Physical and chemical changes, which may or may not be induced by the biota themselves, change the environment, permitting the invasion of the community by other organisms with the subsequent displacement or elimination of the former occupants. Such continuous changes in the community as a whole, made obvious by a sequence of forms is, here, accepted as succession.

Therefore, upon finding a sequence of development that was independent of the seasons, Cirino concluded that ecological succession did occur. My interpretation differs. In spite of the presence of succession, I conclude that establishment of a phase in development is *not* dependent on any environmental change caused by an earlier phase. As mentioned above, the results of this study are generally consistent with those reported by others. This consistency is evident when the populating species are viewed as morphological entities.

Less complex thallus types appear before more complex types: unicellular forms appear before filamentous ones, filamentous forms appear before parenchymatous ones. The unicellular forms, by virtue of reproductive cell division, increase in such numbers that they become the most abundant colonizers very early after denuding. They become well distributed over the space available and form dense stands while the other growth forms are still in juvenile stages of development. Presumably the spores, gametes, or zygotes of the multicellular forms are being constantly transported to the rock surface just as the unicellular forms are. This is where other aspects of time come into play.

First of all the reproductive cells must be present in the water. Furthermore, these cells may attach to the substrate but actual germination may be delayed or even prohibited due to adverse environmental conditions. But for purposes of this interpretation let us assume (1) that the reproductive cells of certain populants are available, (2)

that the physical environment is compatible for growth of these populants, and (3) that germination occurs immediately or soon after
attachment.

Because of the nature of their growth form, filamentous types, such
as *Urospora* and *Ulothrix* would take longer to develop and mature
than diatoms, and parenchymatous types such as *Monostroma* and
Ulva would take even longer. These forms are, in turn, ephemeral in
comparison to the long-lived thalli of *Alaria, Hedophyllum, Fucus,* and
the corallines. In other words, a longer life-span seems to be correlated
with increased specialization in thallus structure. In terms of community development this means that a long-lived individual will
occupy a space for a greater length of time than a short-lived individual. As the long-lived, usually slow-growing alga increases in size,
its space requirement also increases. Ultimately it will take up a certain
growth area within which the establishment of other algae is inhibited.
As the growth space decreases the previously dominant, faster-growing
population gradually decreases in abundance (see Fig. 8) and may
disappear completely or may occur only as epiphytes. In any case, the
actual decrease is due to a short life-span of the attached individuals
as well as to the lack of growth space for the establishment of new
individuals of the same population.

By this interpretation of succession the communities are considered
not to be the result of any intrinsic process of development. The
pattern of development, especially succession, is interpreted to be a
process contingent upon the morphology of the species and the
phenology of the various phases in the life history of the species. The
interplay of these two factors with the all-important factor of space
availability governs the abundance and distribution of the populants.
Heretofore, emphasis on ascribing the intertidal distribution of algal
species has been on physical factors such as exposure, salinity, and
temperature. This study has shown the biological factor of space
competition to be no less significant. Indeed, it may be *the factor* for
the exclusion of some species from certain types of communities.

To summarize, the pattern of development is consistent and predictable, but there is no evidence to indicate that this is an expression
of *ecological succession*. The partial or even total exclusion of a population is concluded not to be due to any changes in habitat originated
by that population. Instead its elimination, partial or otherwise, is
considered to be a consequence of the degree of establishment of the
proceeding population. The successional phenomenon is related to the
morphological nature of the colonizing species, whereby simple forms

are followed by more complex ones. Such a succession is interpreted as being indicative of the relative growth rates and life-spans of the growth forms. The length of time in which a population occupies an area is determined by these factors. The presence or absence of growth space can be a main cause for local distributional patterns, especially for ephemeral species. The dynamic structure of the communities is attributed to species inter-action involving three inter-related factors: (1) the morphology of the organisms; (2) the phenological nature of germination, growth, reproduction, and of spore or gamete release; and (3) the competition for space.

ACKNOWLEDGMENTS

I wish to acknowledge the encouragement and helpful criticism given during the course of the research by Dr. Robert F. Scagel. Financial assistance for the study was provided by the National Research Council of Canada through the Institute of Oceanography, University of British Columbia, and the Defense Research Board of Canada (DRB9520–14).

REFERENCES

1. BEVERIDGE, W. A., and V. J. CHAPMAN. 1950. The zonation of marine algae at Piha, New Zealand, in relation to the tidal factor (studies in intertidal zonation, 2). Pacific Sci. 4(3): 188–201.
2. BOKENHAM, N. A. H. 1938. The colonization of denuded rock surfaces in the intertidal region of the Cape Peninsula. Ann. Natal Mus. 9(1): 47–81.
3. CIRINO, E. F. 1958. Evidence of true succession in marine littoral associations. Ph.D. thesis, Boston Univ. Univ. Microfilms, Ann Arbor, Mich. (L.C. Card No. Mic 58–3095).
4. DEXTER, R. W. 1947. The marine communities of a tidal inlet at Cape Ann, Massachusetts: a study in bio-ecology. Ecol. Monographs 17(3): 261–294.
5. FAHEY, E. M., and M. S. DOTY. 1949. Pioneer colonization on intertidal transects. Biol. Bull. 97(2): 238–239.
6. GORDON, M. S., and H. M. KELLY. 1962. Primary productivity of an Hawaiian coral reef: a critique of flow respirometry in turbulent waters. Ecology 43(3): 473–480.
7. HARTOG, C. den. 1959. The epilithic algal communities occurring along the coast of the Netherlands. Wentia 1: 1–241.
8. ISAAC, W. E. 1949. Studies of South African seaweed vegetation. Trans. Roy. Soc. South Africa 32(2): 125–160.
9. LINDEMAN, R. L. 1942. The trophic-dynamic aspect of ecology. Ecology 23(4): 399–417.
10. MOLINIER, R. 1960. Etude des biocénoses marines du Cap Corse. Vegetatio 9(3): 121–192.
11. MOLINIER, R., and J. PICARD. 1953. Recherches analytiques sur les peuplements littoraux méditerranéens se développant sur substrat solide. Rec. Trav. Stat. Mar. d'Endoume 9: 1–18.

12. MUENSCHER, W. L. C.   1915.   A study of the algal associations of San Juan Island. Publ. Puget Sound Biol. Sta. *1*: 59–84.
13. NORTHCRAFT, R. D.   1948.   Marine algal colonization on the Monterey Peninsula, California. Am. J. Botany *35(7)*: 396–404.
14. ODUM, H. T., and E. P. ODUM.   1955.   Trophic structure and productivity of a windward coral reef community on Eniwetok Atoll. Ecol. Monographs *25(3)*: 291–320.
15. REES, T. K.   1940.   Algal colonization at Mumbles Head. J. Ecol. *28(2)*: 403–437.
16. SARGENT, M. C., and T. S. AUSTIN.   1949.   Organic productivity of an atoll. Trans. Am. Geophys. Union *30(2)*: 245–249.
17. WEAVER, J. E., and F. E. CLEMENTS.   1938.   Plant ecology. 2nd ed. McGraw-Hill, New York.
18. WILSON, O. T.   1925.   Some experimental observations of marine algal successions. Ecology *6(3)*: 303–311.

TABLE I

Developmental events, including condition, just prior to denuding (May 21, 1962) at Victoria Plot I in terms of frequency percentage. The recolonizing species within each phylum are listed first in the general order of their appearance.

Year	1962								1963			
Day	21	5	16	20	14	12	20	12	11	22	26	23
Month	May	Jun	Jun	Jul	Aug	Sep	Oct	Dec	Jan	Feb	Apr	May
Days after denuding		15	26	60	85	114	152	205	235	277	340	367
Chrysophyta												
Amphipleura rutilans	—	100	100	14	—	—	—	—	—	—	—	—
Navicula grevillei	—	—	—	—	—	—	—	11	6	—	—	—
Chlorophyta												
Ulothrix flacca	—	+	—	—	—	—	—	—	—	—	—	—
Urospora mirabilis	—	100	—	—	—	—	—	—	—	—	—	—
Urospora vancouveriana	—	—	100	—	—	—	—	—	—	—	—	—
Urospora wormskioldii	—	—	—	91	11	—	—	—	—	—	—	—
Enteromorpha linza	—	—	—	100	100	100	—	—	—	—	14	6
Monostroma fuscum	14[e]	—	—	—	+	9	100	69	77	97	—	71
Ulva lobata	3[e]	—	—	—	—	—	+	—	—	—	100	60
Spongomorpha spinescens	11[e]	—	—	—	—	—	—	—	—	—	—	—
Phaeophyta												
Costaria costata	6	—	—	—	—	—	—	11	9	11	3	3
Alaria marginata	9[e]	—	—	—	—	—	—	9	6	—	3	14
Heterochordaria abietina	9	—	—	—	—	—	—	—	—	—	—	—
Hedophyllum sessile	9	—	—	—	—	—	—	—	—	—	—	—
Fucus evanescens	6	—	—	—	—	—	—	—	—	—	—	—

TABLE I (Concluded)

Year / Day / Month / Days after denuding	1962 21 May	5 Jun 15	16 Jun 26	20 Jul 60	14 Aug 85	12 Sep 114	20 Oct 152	12 Dec 205	1963 11 Jan 235	22 Feb 277	26 Apr 340	23 May 367
Rhodophyta												
Iridaea cordata	11	—	—	6	9	14	11	17	20	20	23	37
Polysiphonia hendryi	—	—	—	—	—	6	17	+	—	+	—	—
Pterosiphonia gipinnata	—	—	—	—	—	—	—	40	11	83	31	11
Odonthalia floccosa	11	—	—	—	—	—	—	20	54	91	86	97
Prionitis lyallii	26	—	—	—	—	—	—	14	9	6	6	9
Bossiella plumosa and Corallina vancouveriensis	89	—	—	—	—	—	—	3	+	+	51	69
Antithamnion subulatum	—	—	—	—	—	—	—	+	—	—	—	—
Microcladia borealis	9[e]	—	—	—	—	—	—	+	—	3[e]	17	11
Microcladia coulteri	43	—	—	—	—	—	—	—	—	—	—	—
Petrocelis franciscana	—	—	—	—	—	—	—	—	—	—	—	—
Hymenena flabelligera	3	—	—	—	—	—	—	—	—	—	—	6
Porphyra perforata	89[e]	—	—	—	—	—	—	—	—	—	—	3
Polysporolithon reclinatum	6	—	—	—	—	—	—	—	—	—	—	—
Gigartina papillata	—	—	—	—	—	—	—	—	—	—	—	—

— = absent, + = present, e = epiphytic.

TABLE II

Development events, including condition, just prior to denuding (August 14, 1962) at Victoria Plot II in terms of frequency percentage. The recolonizing species within each phylum are listed first in the general order of their appearance.

	Year 1962	1963						
Day	14	12	20	12	11	22	26	23
Month	Aug	Sep	Oct	Dec	Jan	Feb	Apr	May
Days after denuding		29	67	120	150	192	255	282
Chrysophyta								
Amphipleura rutilans	—	100	37	—	—	—	—	—
Navicula grevillei	—	—	—	23	9	60	3	6
Chlorophyta								
Urospora mirabilis	—	100	—	—	—	—	—	—
Enteromorpha linza	3	26	100	29	—	—	26	34
Monostroma fuscum (and)	—	—	—	54			17	
Ulva lobata	3^e	—	—	—	(49)	(43)	—	(74)
Spongomorpha coalita	—	—	—	—	—	—	—	6
Spongomorpha spinescens	11^e	—	—	—	—	—	—	—
Phaeophyta								
Alaria marginata	6	—	—	11	20	37	26	29
Costaria costata	—	—	—	—	—	9	—	—
Petalonia debilis	—	—	—	—	—	—	6	11
Scytosiphon lomentaria	—	—	—	—	—	—	3	—
Colpomenia sinuosa	6^e	—	—	—	—	—	3	—
Hedophyllum sessile	6	—	—	—	—	—	—	—
Ralfsia fungiformis	+	—	—	—	—	—	—	—
Rhodophyta								
Pterosiphonia bipinnata	—	—	—	46	29	49	34	—
Polysiphonia hendryi	—	—	—	+	—	3	+	60
Iridaea cordata	43	—	—	—	9	11	37	29
Odonthalia floccosa	—	—	—	—	—	29	29	17
Bossiella plumosa and								
Corallina vancouveriensis	71	—	—	—	—	—	20	11
Callophyllis sp.	—	—	—	—	—	—	—	3
Polyporolithon reclinatum	71^e	—	—	—	—	—	—	—
Petrocelis franciscana	37	—	—	—	—	—	—	—
Prionitis lyallii	31	—	—	—	—	—	—	—
Microcladia borealis	17^{es}	—	—	—	—	—	—	—
Microcladia coulteri	6^e	—	—	—	—	—	—	—
Hymenena flabelligera	3	—	—	—	—	—	—	—
Laurencia spectabilis	3	—	—	—	—	—	—	—

— = absent, + = present, e = epiphytic, es = epiphytic and saxicolous.

TABLE III

Developmental events, including condition, just prior to denuding (February 22, 1963) at Victoria Plot III in terms of frequency percentage. The recolonizing species within each phylum are listed first in the general order of their appearance.

Year / Day / Month / Days after denuding	1963 22 Feb	26 Apr 63	23 May 90	8 Jun 106	6 Jul 134	5 Aug 164	18 Aug 177	1 Sep 191	7 Oct 227	4 Nov 255	1 Dec 282	28 Dec 309	1964 26 Jan 338
Chrysophyta													
Amphipleura rutilans	—	97	—	—	—	—	—	—	—	—	—	—	—
Navicula grevillei	37[es]	—	—	—	—	—	—	—	—	—	—	—	11
Chlorophyta													
Urospora wormskioldii	—	80	—	—	—	—	—	—	—	—	—	—	—
Monostroma fuscum (and)	6	69	91	83	100	100	100	100	—	—	—	—	—
Ulva lobata	—	—	—	—	—	—	—	100	(80)	(86)	(100)	(94)	(94)
Spongomorpha coalita	—	37	97	97	97	74	74	—	—	—	—	—	—
Enteromorpha linza	—	14	54	60	23	17	23	—	—	—	—	—	—
Spongomorpha spinescens	60[es]	—	—	—	—	—	—	—	—	—	—	—	—
Monostroma arcticum	3[e]	—	—	—	—	—	—	—	—	—	—	—	—
Phaeophyta													
Petalonia debilis	—	—	3	—	—	—	—	—	—	—	—	—	—
Alaria marginata	23	—	—	—	—	—	—	—	—	—	—	—	—
Desmarestia munda	3	—	—	—	—	—	—	—	—	—	—	—	—
Rhodophyta													
Pterosiphonia bipinnata	14	9	43	29	54	9	9	—	—	—	43	94	49
Iridaea cordata	20	—	6	3	—	6	—	—	—	—	—	—	—
Prionitis lyallii	6	—	—	—	3	3	3	6	—	—	—	—	—
Bossiella plumosa and *Corallina vancouveriensis*	54	—	—	—	—	—	—	—	—	—	—	—	—
Odonthalia floccosa	—	—	—	—	—	—	—	—	—	—	6	9	+
Polyporolithon reclinatum	54[e]	—	—	—	—	—	—	—	—	—	—	9	—
Petrocelis franciscana	23	—	—	—	—	—	—	—	—	—	—	—	—
Microcladia borealis	20	—	—	—	—	—	—	—	—	—	—	—	—

— = absent, + = present, e = epiphytic, es = epiphytic and saxicolous.

TABLE IV

Development events, including condition, just prior to denuding (June 8, 1963) at Victoria Plot IV in terms of frequency percentage. The recolonizing species within each phylum are listed first in the general order of their appearance.

	Year 1963									1964
Day	8	6	5	18	1	7	4	1	28	26
Month	Jun	Jul	Aug	Aug	Sep	Oct	Nov	Dec	Dec	Jan
Days after denuding		28	58	71	85	121	149	176	203	232
Chrysophyta										
Amphipleura rutilans	—	100	69	—	—	—	—	—	—	—
Navicula grevillei	—	—	—	—	—	—	—	100	100	97
Chlorophyta										
Urospora wormskioldii	—	26	—	—	—	—	—	—	—	—
Enteromorpha linza	—	—	100	100	100	100	100	+	—	—
Spongomorpha coalita	6	—	—	6	—	—	—	—	—	—
Monostroma fuscum (and)	34^e	—	—	—	—	—	—	—	—	—
Ulva lobata	—	—	—	—	—	(43)	100	100	100	97
Phaeophyta										
Alaria marginata	34^{es}	—	—	—	—	—	—	11	11	11
Petalonia debilis	—	—	—	—	—	—	—	6	9	3
Costaria costata	—	—	—	—	—	—	—	3	—	—
Rhodophyta										
Iridaea cordata	14	—	9	14	—	6	—	11	9	14
Bossiella plumosa and										
Corallina vancouveriensis	74	—	—	6	—	—	—	—	—	—
Petrocelis franciscana	34	—	—	6	—	—	—	—	—	—
Antithamnion subulatum	—	—	—	—	—	—	—	37	—	—
Odonthalia floccosa	26	—	—	—	—	—	—	11	—	—
Prionitis lyallii	—	—	—	—	—	—	—	3	—	3
Pterosiphonia bipinnata	—	—	—	—	—	—	—	—	—	11
Polyporolithon reclinatum	74^e	—	—	—	—	—	—	—	—	—
Microcladia borealis	23^{es}	—	—	—	—	—	—	—	—	—
Hymenena flabelligera	6	—	—	—	—	—	—	—	—	—
Halosaccion glandiforme	3^e	—	—	—	—	—	—	—	—	—

— = absent, + = present, e = epiphytic, es = epiphytic and saxicolous.

TABLE V

Developmental events, including condition, just prior to denuding (August 5, 1963) at Victoria Plot V in terms of frequency percentage. The recolonizing species within each phylum are listed first in the general order of their appearance.

	Year 1963							Year 1964
Day	5	18	1	7	4	1	28	26
Month	Aug	Aug	Sep	Oct	Nov	Dec	Dec	Jan
Days after denuding		13	27	63	91	118	145	174
Chrysophyta								
Amphipleura rutilans	—	100	100	—	—	—	—	—
Navicula grevillei	—	—	—	3	40	86	100	66
Chlorophyta								
Enteromorpha linza	—	—	46	86	94	80	—	—
Monostroma fuscum (and)		—	—	—	51	—	—	—
Ulva lobata	(20es)	—	—	—	—	37	94	54
Phaeophyta								
Petalonia debilis	—	—	—	—	—	—	3	—
Alaria marginata	31	—	—	—	—	—	—	9
Hedophyllum sessile	6	—	—	—	—	—	—	—
Rhodophyta								
Iridaea cordata	20es	—	—	—	—	20	3	11
Prionitis lyallii	11	—	—	—	—	3	—	—
Polyporolithon reclinatum	74e	—	—	—	—	—	—	—
Bossiella plumosa and								
Corallina vancouveriensis	74	—	—	—	—	—	—	—
Odonthalia floccosa	31	—	—	—	—	—	—	—
Hymenena flabelligera	9	—	—	—	—	—	—	—
Cryptonemia obovata	3	—	—	—	—	—	—	—
Rhodomela larix	3	—	—	—	—	—	—	—

— = absent, e = epiphytic, es = epiphytic and saxicolous.

TABLE VI

Developmental events, including condition, just prior to denuding (November 4, 1963) at Victoria Plot VI in terms of frequency percentage. The recolonizing species within each phylum are listed first in the general order of their appearance.

	Year	1963		1964
	Day	4	28	26
	Month	Nov	Dec	Jan
Days after denuding			27	56
Chlorophyta				
Monostroma fuscum		9[es]	—	—
Phaeophyta				
Ralfsia fungiformis		—	80	—
Alaria marginata		63[es]	—	6
Rhodophyta				
Antithamnion subulatum		—	—	14
Prionitis lyalli		—	—	3
Polyporolithon reclinatum		86[e]	—	—
Bossiella plumosa and				
Corallina vancouveriensis		86	—	—
Prionitis lanceolata		6	—	—
Petrocelis franciscana		6	—	—
Microcladia coulteri		6[e]	—	—
Iridaea cordata		3	—	—
Laurencia spectabilis		3	—	—

— = absent, e = epiphytic, es = epiphytic and saxicolous.

NOTE: The community analyzed before denuding is dated November 4. However, the actual completion of the denuding procedure did not take place until December 1. Therefore, the days after denuding begin from the latter date.

TABLE VII

Developmental events, including condition, just prior to denuding (June 4, 1962) at Glacier Point in terms of frequency percentage. The recolonizing species within each phylum are listed first in the general order of their appearance.

Year / Day Month (Days after denuding)	1962 Jun	17 Jun (13)	21 Jul (47)	14 Aug (71)	12 Sep (100)	20 Oct (138)	12 Dec (191)	27 Dec (206)	11 Jan 1963 (221)	21 Feb (262)	27 Apr (327)	24 May (354)	9 Jun (370)	7 Jul (398)	4 Aug (426)	17 Aug (439)	2 Sep (455)	6 Oct (489)	3 Nov (517)	1 Dec (545)	15 Jan 1964 (590)
Chrysophyta																					
Amphipleura rutilans	—	100	—	+	—	—	27	—	—	53	—	—	—	—	—	—	—	—	—	—	—
Navicula grevillei	—	—	—	—	—	—	—	—	—	53	—	—	—	—	—	—	—	—	—	—	—
Chlorophyta																					
Ulothrix flacca	—	100	80	93	93	+	87	87	87	80	80	87	73	73	80	60	67	13	—	—	—
Enteromorpha linza	—	—	53	—	—	—	—	—	—	53	—	—	—	—	—	—	—	—	—	—	—
Urospora wormskioldii	—	—	—	—	—	—	—	—	—	—	—	—	—	—	—	—	—	—	—	—	—
Urospora mirabilis	—	—	—	40	—	—	40	47	40	27	47	87	(40)	(53)	40	(67)	53	—	53	13	—
Ulva lobata (and) Ulva stenophylla	13es	—	—	—	—	—	—	—	—	60	—	—	—	—	—	—	80	80	53	13	7
Spongomorpha coalita	13	—	—	—	—	—	—	—	—	80	80	73	67	67	53	53	27	27	—	—	—
Monostroma arcticum	7e	—	—	—	—	—	—	—	—	—	—	—	—	—	—	—	—	—	—	—	—
Phaeophyta																					
Ralfsia fungiformis	13	—	—	—	—	—	7	—	—	—	7	—	—	—	—	—	—	20	—	—	13
Petalonia debilis	27	—	—	—	—	—	—	—	—	—	7	7	7	—	7	7	7	—	—	—	7
Alaria marginata	—	—	—	—	—	—	—	—	—	—	33	33	37	20	20	7	7	20	—	13	13
Laminaria cuneifolia	7	—	—	—	—	—	—	—	—	—	—	—	—	—	—	—	—	—	—	—	—
Haplogloia andersonii	27	—	—	—	—	—	—	—	—	—	—	—	—	—	—	—	—	—	—	—	—
Hedophyllum sessile	27	—	—	—	—	—	—	—	—	—	—	7	7	7	7	—	—	—	—	—	—
Fucus evanescens	7	—	—	—	—	—	—	—	—	—	—	—	—	—	—	—	—	—	—	—	—
Cystoseira geminata	7	—	—	—	—	—	—	—	—	—	—	—	—	—	—	—	—	—	—	—	—
Egregia menziesii	7	—	—	—	—	—	—	—	—	—	—	—	—	—	—	—	—	—	—	—	—
Coilodesme californica	7e	—	—	—	—	—	—	—	—	—	—	—	—	—	—	—	—	—	—	—	—
Rhodophyta																					
Iridaea cordata	60	—	—	—	—	—	—	7	13	—	7	—	7	20	13	7	13	20	20	27	7
Microcladia borealis	13	—	—	—	—	—	—	—	20	—	33	—	—	—	7	7	7	20	20	27	27
Odonthalia floccosa	33es	—	—	—	—	—	—	—	20	—	20	20	—	—	13	13	7	20	33	27	27
Petrocelis franciscana	40	—	—	—	—	—	—	—	—	13	20	20	13	—	7	+	—	—	—	—	—
Ptilota filicina	7	—	—	—	—	—	—	—	—	—	7	13	—	—	—	—	7e	7	—	—	—
Porphyra perforata	13es	—	—	—	—	—	—	—	—	—	—	—	13	—	7	—	—	—	—	—	—
Plocamium oregonum	—	—	—	—	—	—	—	—	—	—	—	—	20	13	—	—	—	—	—	—	—
Bossiella plumosa and Corallina vancouveriensis	40	—	—	—	—	—	—	—	—	—	—	7	7	—	20	+	+	+	+	+	+
Plocamium pacificum	27	—	—	—	—	—	—	—	—	—	—	—	—	—	—	—	7	—	—	—	—
Bangia fuscopurpurea	27	—	—	—	—	—	—	—	—	—	—	—	—	—	—	—	7	27	33	27	—
Pterosiphonia bipinnata	—	—	—	—	—	—	—	—	—	—	—	—	—	—	—	—	—	7	—	—	—
Delesseria decipiens	+e	—	—	—	—	—	—	—	—	—	—	—	—	—	—	—	—	+	—	—	—
Halosaccion glandiforme	40e	—	—	—	—	—	—	—	—	—	—	—	—	—	—	—	—	—	—	—	—
Polysiphonia reclinatum	20es	—	—	—	—	—	—	—	—	—	—	—	—	—	—	—	—	—	—	—	—
Rhodomela larix	20	—	—	—	—	—	—	—	—	—	—	—	—	—	—	—	—	—	—	—	—
Prionitis lyallii	13e	—	—	—	—	—	—	—	—	—	—	—	—	—	—	—	—	—	—	—	—
Microcladia coulteri	7	—	—	—	—	—	—	—	—	—	—	—	—	—	—	—	—	—	—	—	—
Hymenena flabelligera	—	—	—	—	—	—	—	—	—	—	—	—	—	—	—	—	—	—	—	—	—

— = absent, + = present, e = epiphytic, es = epiphytic and saxicolous.

TABLE VIII

Developmental events, including condition, just prior to denuding (June 3, 1962) at Port Renfrew in terms of frequency percentage. The recolonizing species within each phylum are listed first in the general order of their appearance.

Year	1962					1963					
Day	3	16	20	19	11	10	3	21	27	24	7
Month	Jun	Jun	Jul	Oct	Dec	Jan	Feb	Feb	Apr	May	Jul
Days after denuding		13	47	138	191	221	245	263	328	355	399
Chlorophyta											
Enteromorpha linza	—	7	27	—	—	—	—	—	—	—	—
Rhizoclonium riparium	40	+	—	—	—	—	+	—	—	—	—
Ulva lactuca	—	—	—	100	100	73	+	53[es]	7	13	—
Spongomorpha spinescens	—	—	—	—	—	—	—	—	7	—	—
Spongomorpha coalita	7	—	—	—	—	—	—	—	—	—	—
Phaeophyta											
Petalonia debilis	—	—	—	100	73	27	+	47	—	—	—
Fucus evanescens	93	—	—	20	20	27	+	13[e]	53	100	100
Ectocarpus sp.	—	—	—	—	—	—	—	—	—	—	—
Scytosiphon lomentaria	—	—	—	—	—	—	—	—	7	—	—
Leathesia difformis	7	—	—	—	—	—	—	—	—	—	—
Rhodophyta											
Bangia fuscopurpurea	—	+	—	—	—	—	—	—	—	—	—
Petrocelis franciscana	—	—	—	—	—	—	7	—	—	—	—
Pterosiphonia bipinnata (and)	(73)	—	—	—	—	—	—	—	53	73	87
Polysiphonia hendryi	60	—	—	—	—	—	—	—	—	—	+
Microcladia borealis	7	—	—	—	—	—	—	—	20	—	—
Iridaea cordata	7	—	—	—	—	—	—	—	—	—	13
Halosaccion glandiforme	20	—	—	—	—	—	—	—	—	—	—
Gigartina papillata	7	—	—	—	—	—	—	—	—	—	—

— = absent, + = present, e = epiphytic, es = epiphytic and saxicolous.

TABLE IX

Thallus growth and stage of maturity from the time of germination as related to days within which they occurred.

Species	Growth Period (days within)	Thallus Height (cm)	R = Reproductive V = Vegetative
Chrysophyta			
Amphipleura rutilans	15	11.0	—
Navicula grevillei	27	9.0	—
Chlorophyta			
Ulothrix flacca	15	0.15	—
Urospora mirabilis	15	2.2	—
Urospora vancouveriana	11	5.0	—
Urospora wormskioldii	26	10.0	—
Enteromorpha linza	30	37.0	R
Monostroma fuscum	29	9.0	R
Ulva lobata	30	27.0	R
Spongomorpha coalita	13	4.0	R
Phaeophyta			
Haplogloia andersonii	27	24.0	R
Petalonia debilis	34	10.0	R
*Costaria costata	30	21.0	V
*Hedophyllum sessile	28	33.0	V
*Alaria marginata	65	135.0	V
Rhodophyta			
Bangia fuscopurpurea	16	6.0	R
Porphyra perforata	16	34.0	R
*Bossiella plumosa			
basal crust	119	(1.1 width)	—
erect shoots	112	0.7	V
*Prionitis lyallii	30	11.0	V
*Iridaea cordata	15	15.0	R
Hymenena flabelligera	27	11.0	V
Antithamnion subulatum	27	2.0	R
Polysiphonia hendryi	29	3.0	R
Pterosiphonia bipinnata	28	7.0	R
*Odonthalia floccosa	13	3.0	V

NOTE: A species with an asterisk indicates that the data for that species were obtained from individual plants. For other species the data were derived from a population; hence, thallus height is the maximum height found within a population, and the time of reproduction is when the population had reproducing individuals.

T. A. STEEVES, R. T. COUPLAND,
AND M. V. S. RAJU

Vegetative Propagation in Relation to the Aggressiveness of Species

IN THE STUDY OF EVOLUTION, it is customary to place particular emphasis upon sexual methods of reproduction. From the genetic point of view it is certainly valid to do this; and, in fact, vegetative methods of reproduction, however effective they may be in a particular situation, are bound to be stagnating in the long run to the course of evolutionary change. In considering the development of floras, however, vegetative reproduction may assume profound importance, since the advantages offered to particular species by such means of propagation, especially under adverse conditions, may significantly influence the abundance of occurrence of these species in a plant population, or, in fact, whether they occur at all.

In his comprehensive treatise, "The Reproductive Capacity of Plants," E. J. Salisbury (27) has cited numerous examples of the determining role of vegetative multiplication in the distribution of particular species, and hence in the composition of populations. Of the perennial species which are common in most or all of the counties and vice-counties of Great Britain, there are twice as many species with pronounced vegetative propagation as there are species with slight or no capacity for vegetative increase. For example, among the species of *Hypericum* in Britain, those with extensive vegetative propagation (notably *H. perforatum*) are much more abundant even though their reproductive capacity by seeds is distinctly lower than that of less abundant species. Many species thrive and multiply by vegetative means under conditions in which reproduction by seeds is prevented, either because circumstances are sub-minimal for flowering or fruiting or because seed germination or seedling establishment is reduced or eliminated. Thus, flower or seed production may be uncommon in species growing near the extremes of their geographical or altitudinal ranges, or locally thriving under deep shade, while seedlings may be found rarely in instances in which species, such as *Cirsium arvense* or *Linaria vulgaris*, invade closed grassland. In a similar vein, it is interesting to note that the rather widespread distribution and local abundance of temperate species of *Lycopodium* must depend upon vigorous vegetative spread, since sexual reproduction in these species is accomplished with extreme rarity. Perhaps even more striking is the case of bracken, *Pteridium aquilinum*, which, although a fern, heads the list of noxious weeds in many areas of the world because of the almost irresistible vigour of its ramifying rhizome system.

Any botanist, agriculturist, or naturalist could expand this list of examples almost indefinitely and the implications are clear. Understanding of local plant communities or larger regional floras and the changes which they undergo in response to natural or human influences cannot be achieved without serious consideration of the occurrence of vegetative mechanisms of reproduction. In this paper it will not be possible to review the general field of vegetative reproduction. It is intended, rather, to select a few topics for more intensive discussion and to review some recent studies in Saskatchewan which pertain to this subject.

THE NATURE OF VEGETATIVE PROPAGATION

Vegetative propagation is a type of asexual reproduction which is usually considered to be distinct from spore production; but if all groups of plants are taken into consideration this distinction is difficult to maintain. Throughout the vascular plants, however, spore formation occurs in a particular relationship to meiosis in the sexual reproductive cycle and is consequently clearly delimited from any vegetative type of multiplication. Vegetative propagation may ordinarily be considered to involve a fragmentation of the body of the plant, the separation of a fragment which establishes a new individual. However, the processes which are capable of accomplishing propagation do not necessarily lead to the separation of new individuals, and vegetative spread may occur effectively whether or not separation takes place.

Among the vascular plants (with which we are primarily concerned here) there are numerous mechanisms by which vegetative multiplication is accomplished. In aquatic plants, such as *Elodea*, the natural breaking off of an unmodified fragment which subsequently establishes a new individual is a common phenomenon and is instrumental in their often rapid spread. In terrestrial forms, although many species can be propagated artificially by the isolation of unmodified vegetative cuttings, the natural detachment of ordinary vegetative fragments is not common. It has been reported by Lyon (20) as occurring in *Selaginella rupestris* and apparently also occurs in some species of *Salix* growing in moist habitats. In some woody species, however, lower branches in contact with the soil may form roots and thus become separate growth centres in the process known as layering. Subsequent detachment sometimes results in the establishment of new individuals. Natural propagation is more commonly accomplished by the production of bulbils, modified buds which become detached and establish new individuals. The formation of small bulbs or corms as axillary buds on parent bulbs or corms is a comparable phenomenon.

Many plants produce horizontal stems which, even if unmodified, serve to accomplish the spread of the plant if, as in many cucurbits, they produce adventitious roots along the stem. If branches become detached by breaking or by death and decay, new individuals are formed. In bracken the entire stem system is subterranean, the leaves alone appearing above ground; and the vigorous spread of the fern is accomplished by the growth and ramification of this system. In some species the shoot system is dimorphic, consisting of leafy, upright shoots and horizontal shoots, often with reduced leaves and unusually long internodes which function as propagating runners or rhizomes. Leafy aerial shoots are borne laterally or develop terminally from the horizontal shoots. Some of the most successful species, as far as vegetative multiplication is concerned, accomplish their spread by means of rhizomes or runners. The ostrich fern, *Pteretis pensylvanica*, presents an interesting case of a dimorphic shoot system which is entirely rhizomatous. The main axis is a short shoot, bearing large foliage fronds and sporophylls which expand above ground, whereas the lateral axes, or side shoots, have reduced leaves and elongate internodes. After a side shoot apex has been extended for some distance from the main axis, it becomes a short shoot and produces a crown of expanded leaves. In all such cases, subsidiary shoots remain attached to the parent for a variable period, often becoming separate individuals by the severing of the connection through death and decay, or by mechanical disruption.

Leaves serve as propagating devices perhaps less frequently, but there are many familiar examples of this phenomenon. In plants such as *Kalanchoe*, plantlets which arise from leaf tissues, often in great profusion, may become detached to establish new individuals or, as in the walking fern, *Camptosorus*, they may arise from the leaf in contact with the soil and establish new growth centres which only later become separate individuals.

Among the most interesting cases of vegetative multiplication, from the morphogenetic as well as the ecological point of view, are those which involve the initiation of adventitious shoots upon roots (Fig. 1). Root buds are often regarded as an anomaly except under artificial conditions; but their occurrence is, in fact, widespread. Because roots often attain considerable depths in the soil, undesirable species which produce root buds may be extremely difficult to control and nearly impossible to eradicate (Selleck *et al.*, 28). Moreover, since roots may achieve considerable horizontal extension, the rate of spread by means of propagating roots is often very rapid (Best, 4; Frazier, 13). Finally, the capacity of roots to produce stems might be of significance in the survival of some species in episodes of adversity, such as drought and fire, when more shallowly placed rhizome systems may be destroyed. Much of the recent work in Saskatchewan that will be reviewed in this paper concerns perennial species which propagate by means of root buds.

SOME EXAMPLES OF VEGETATIVE PROPAGATION

In this consideration of vegetative propagation the authors have elected not to review a wide range of literature in the vain hope of achieving complete coverage, but rather to consider several examples with which they have some familiarity, either through their own observations or through those of their colleagues. It is hoped that these examples will serve to illustrate a few of the basic principles involved, and some of the difficulties encountered, in the study of vegetative multiplication, as well as to suggest general implications for the evolution of Canada's flora.

Black spruce (*Picea mariana*) is one of the major tree species of Canada and occurs in vast stands in the boreal forest. For many years it has been known that this species reproduces vegetatively by layering

15 cm

FIGURE 1. A spreading, shallow root of *Populus balsamifera* with two well-developed shoots.

FIGURE 2. A root system of *Euphorbia esula* showing development of shoots on long roots at the point where they turn vertically downward.

(Cooper, 7; Fuller, 14). When lower branches become overgrown by mosses, or otherwise buried, they may develop adventitious roots. The branch tips then assume a vertical growth habit and new growth centres are thus formed. There seems to be no general agreement as to the effectiveness of this process in propagating the species. Some workers (Place, 23; Vincent, 33) regard it as a major method in certain habitats, others relegate it to the realm of insignificance. Recently a new suggestion has been made which warrants further investigation. LeBlanc (18), working in Quebec, has reported that in black spruce, shoots may arise from shallow roots and subsequently develop into independent plants. According to the report this "rootling" production may be a significant factor in reproduction, having in the past been mistaken for layering. Horton and Lees (16) have reached a similar conclusion in a study in Alberta. These accounts of vegetative reproduction in black spruce raise very important questions about the geography and ecology of this important component of Canada's flora, questions which have scarcely been considered up to the present time.

Propagation by means of root shoots is apparently not a rare phenomenon among dicotyledonous tree species, sometimes almost to the exclusion of reproduction by seed (Salisbury, 27). The aspen poplar, *Populus tremuloides*, in common with at least some other species of the genus, manifests this property to a marked degree, a fact which might be related to its status as the most widely distributed tree in North America. In a recent study in Saskatchewan, Maini (21) has investigated the ecology of this species in the aspen grove region where the boreal forest and grasslands meet. The results of this analysis offer strong support to the thesis that vegetative multiplication may be an important consideration in the interpretation of plant associations. Examinations of aspen clumps in various stages of expansion revealed that spreading is always accomplished by means of shoots produced upon relatively shallow horizontal roots. Burning or cutting of the boles is followed by rapid regeneration from the roots. It is interesting to note that an extensive search during this study failed to reveal a single seedling, although viable seeds were produced. Examination of this species farther northward in the boreal forest zone, reveals that vegetative multiplication is again widespread. The rapid and uniform regeneration after fire attests to this. However, in the forest zone one can find seedlings occasionally in disturbed locations. Thus it seems that seeds may serve to establish new aspen localities in the boreal forest, but vegetative multiplication undoubtedly plays the major role in the expansion of existing stands and their regeneration after fire. South of the forest, however, seeds seem not to function; and the existing scattered groves must have had an ancient origin, perhaps extending back in time to some particular period in post-glacial history when climatic conditions more nearly resembled those of the forest zone today. For centuries these groves must have persisted, receding in unfavourable periods, expanding vegetatively when conditions improved, repeatedly being destroyed by the vast fires which swept the prairies before the land was claimed for agriculture, and each time being renewed by the regenerative activity of the root system. It has been concluded that the greater prominence of aspen groves today than at the time of first settlement reflects the virtual elimination of fire from the prairie scene.

Another striking example of the prominent role of vegetative multiplication is seen in the aggressiveness and persistence of a number of introduced perennial dicotyledonous herbs which constitute some of the most menacing weeds of the Canadian prairies. The invasiveness of these species, their resistance to control methods, both mechanical and chemical, and their persistence during adverse climatic phases at the expense of less vigorous but more useful species, causes them to be an important item in the agricultural economy of the plains. Several of these species have been the objects of intensive life-history studies at the University of Saskatchewan, and much has been learned about their morphology and ecology. A review of the information obtained about one of the most vigorous of these plants, leafy spurge, *Euphorbia esula*, will serve to illustrate the significance of vegetative multiplication in their biological success.

Leafy spurge was first discovered in North America in 1827, but was not recognized in western Canada until the early part of the twentieth century (Selleck *et al.*, 28). It has been estimated that it presently infests between 35,000 and 40,000 acres in Canada alone, much of this being otherwise valuable agricultural land. Leafy spurge, while also reproducing by seed, is characterized by the production of numerous adventitious buds on the shallower portions of its root system which lead to extensive vegetative spread in a variety of habitats.

In and around infestations of leafy spurge, young seedlings are ordinarily easily found if moisture conditions are favourable, the bulk of the germination occurring in early spring. The primary root grows vertically downward, quickly establishing the seedling, and under field conditions penetrations to a depth of 39 inches have been reported four months after germination (Selleck *et al.*, 28). The shoot also develops rapidly; within 10 to 15 days adventitious buds capable of replacing the primary axis, if this is destroyed, develop on the hypocotyl. The rate of development of the root system is extremely variable, depending upon moisture conditions and, to a very marked extent, upon competition with other vegetation. In areas with a dense vegetative cover, the seedling roots develop slowly and usually succumb before the end of the first season. In denuded areas, on the other hand, an extensive root system is established which may persist, even if the shoot dies back from drought or is killed by frost (Raju *et al.*, 24). The primary root is characterized by vigorous growth which is potentially unlimited; and it also increases in thickness through cambial activity. By contrast, the laterals which develop on it are of limited terminal growth and do not undergo secondary thickening. They ordinarily have a short life-span in contrast to the persistent primary root. The seedling root system is thus heterorhizic, the primary root being a long root and the laterals being short roots (Raju *et al.*, 24). Before the end of the first season, in areas free of competition, the root system begins to spread by the formation of lateral long roots which grow horizontally for some distance before turning to a vertical direction. It is an interesting point that lateral long roots are not initiated at any location on the primary root until cambial activity has begun at that level, although it is not clear that the root primordia necessarily arise from secondary tissues.

As the root system expands, it remains pronouncedly heterorhizic, consisting of a framework of vertical, horizontal, and oblique long roots bearing numerous determinate short roots upon them. The production of buds on certain of the roots leads to the formation of new growth centres which may in time become separate individuals and from which the lateral spread of the root system continues. A survey of the density of root development in typical infestations has been carried out in Saskatchewan (Coupland and Alex, 9). Although density decreases with depth, roots have been traced to depths in excess of 10 feet (Raju *et al.*, 24) in Saskatchewan, and Bakke (3) has reported penetration to 15 feet in Iowa. In only one of 32 sites examined in Saskatchewan did roots fail to reach a depth of 48 inches (Coupland and Alex, 9). The mean dry weight of underground structures to a depth of 48 inches was calculated to be 8,492 pounds per acre, some 56 per cent of this occurring in the 6-inch surface layer, but this figure included the basal portions of shoots as well as roots.

The significance of this extensive root system in relation to vegetative multiplication becomes clear when its reproductive capacity is examined. In seedlings of leafy spurge, buds are often formed on the primary root before the end of the first season. These, together with those of the hypocotyl, serve to re-establish a shoot system when the original is destroyed. Buds on the primary root arise only after cambial activity has begun at a particular level, and lateral short roots which have no cambium have never been seen to produce a bud at any stage in the development of the root system. When lateral long roots develop, these too produce shoot buds, and the process of bud formation continues throughout the expansion of the root system. In shallower levels of the soil a long root ordinarily grows horizontally for some distance and then turns to a vertical direction of growth. Frequently a bud is initiated at the point of turning down (Fig. 2). If this produces a shoot, a new centre is established with a shoot and a main root, which may become a separate individual if the connection to the parent plant is lost. After several seasons of growth, it is difficult to distinguish such plants from those of seedling origin. Subsequently, further bud development may occur on both the horizontal and the vertical portions of the root, and lateral long roots arise which continue the process of spreading. The dependence of both buds and long roots upon the prior occurrence of secondary growth is an interesting correlation. In old roots it is evident that both of these organs arise from secondary phloem (Raju et al., 25). In younger roots the histological picture is less clear because of the participation of the pericycle which proliferates somewhat in those roots which have cambial activity.

The distribution of buds on the root system has also been investigated and considerable variation has been found (Coupland and Alex, 10). Maximum depths at which buds were found varied from 12 to 68 inches in different sites and on different roots in the same site and there are reports of occasional buds at depths as great as 7 feet (Bakke, 3). The density of bud formation decreases with depth in the soil and the decrease is rather sharp below the first 6 inches. Nonetheless, roots at depths of 3 to 4 feet frequently bear buds in significant numbers. Under undisturbed conditions, many of the buds, especially those at deeper levels, seem never to expand as leafy shoots, most of the shoots having their origin from roots within 1 foot of the surface. Occasionally shoots do develop at deeper levels, some of which reach the surface, and some of which do not. Disturbance, however, modifies the situation considerably. In one series of experiments (Coupland et al., 11) in which excavations of various depths were lined with steel cribbing and filled with tamped, root-free soil, emergence of shoots regularly occurred from depths of 2 feet in one year and a few developed from 3 feet. Moreover, it has been shown (Raju *et al.*, 25) that if segments of roots are planted in shallow flats in a greenhouse, shoots are regenerated from pieces having their origin at depths as great as 9 feet. The significant point here is that in many cases no buds were present when the fragments were severed; and shoots arose *de novo* from root tissues. The well-known difficulties experienced in attempting to control leafy spurge by tillage are recalled by these observations.

Leafy spurge illustrates vegetative propagation in a highly developed state, and there can be little doubt that its remarkable invasiveness and persistence are related to this property. It also illustrates some of the important considerations which must be dealt with in studying this type of multiplication. In this species, reproduction by seeds, which occurs successfully under favourable circumstances, serves to colonize new sites; whereas vegetative propagation, continuing in severe competition with other species and under various adversities of environment, increases the size of colonies and enhances persistence even under unfavourable circumstances.

The list of introduced perennial herbaceous dicotyledons that have distinguished themselves by their great capacity for vegetative spread in Saskatchewan includes ten species in addition to leafy spurge. These are *Cardaria* spp. (at least two species), *Centaurea repens*, *Cirsium arvense*, *Convolulus arvensis* (Best, 4), *Linaria dalmatica*, L. *vulgaris* (Charleton, 6; Coupland *et al.*, 12), *Lychnis alba*, *Rumex acetosella*, and *Sonchus arvensis*. A review of the literature, together with the authors' own observations, has revealed that all of these plants are characterized by the formation of root shoots and multiply vigorously by this means. These observations suggested the possibility that propagation by roots capable of initiating adventitious shoots in the absence of injury or disturbance might be restricted to these introduced species among the herbaceous dicotyledons of the region and might explain their apparent greater vigour as compared to native species. The importance of this mechanism in aspen among the woody species was already clear.

With this possibility in mind, a preliminary survey of perennial dicotyledons was carried out in the prairies and forest border of southern Saskatchewan to ascertain the occurrence of root buds in both native and introduced species (*Raju et al.*, 26). The surprising result of this survey, which was not exhaustive, was that 38 species were discovered with adventitious shoots or buds on their roots in the absence of any evident injury or disturbance. These species are distributed through 19 families of dicotyledons and include plants native in various parts of the northern hemisphere, indicating that the phenomenon is probably widespread both taxonomically and geographically (Table I). Eleven of the twelve species which are introduced are very persistent field weeds in western Canada and include all of the "persistent perennials" which have been troublesome in Saskatchewan because of their resistance to intensive tillage. On the other hand, 26 species were found which are considered to be native to the area. Most of these are recognized as vigorous and abundant members of the flora, and three of the seven most abundant dicotyledons on the mixed prairie grasslands of southern Saskatchewan are included (Coupland, 8). However, only two, *Lactuca pulchella* and *Iva axillaris*, have been especially difficult to control in cultivated fields.

TABLE I

THE OCCURRENCE OF ROOT-BUD–BEARING PERENNIAL DICOTYLEDONS IN SASKATCHEWAN

	Families	Genera	All Species	Weedy Species in Cropland
Native			26	4
Introduced			12	11
Total	19	31	38	15

In general, then, it appears that the ability to produce adventitious root shoots is associated with aggressiveness in both native and introduced prairie species. The questions raised by the results of the survey are perhaps more important than any conclusions. Why, for example, are the introduced species as a group so much more aggressive than most of the native species, and why do they persist more tenaciously in cultivated areas? The ability to form root shoots seems to be an essential component of the aggressiveness and persistence of the introduced weeds; but of the native species having the same characteristic most have not persisted under tillage. Possibly the difference may lie in the general area of lack of biological control of introduced organisms, or it might be that the introduced weeds represent a highly selected group of species, or perhaps even strains of generally less vigorous species, which have become established in alien areas because of their vigour. In any event, comparative analysis of their propagating mechanisms should provide an interesting insight into the relationships of this phenomenon to aggressiveness. The numbers of buds produced per root unit, or the circumstances, general or specialized, under which buds are initiated, might be significant factors. Also the nature of the root system, whether spreading or more vertical in type, could be of importance. Finally, histological details of bud initiation should be examined to determine if there are any general relationships between patterns of development and aggressiveness and persistence of species. One interesting sidelight might be mentioned. At least five of the species found in this survey that produced root shoots also formed rhizomes. Thus the relative importance and success of these two methods of propagation can be compared in the same species under a variety of conditions.

DISCUSSION

There are several general considerations relating to vegetative multiplication which are suggested by the specific instances described in this paper. The phenomenon of vegetative propagation is a reflection of the remarkable regenerative capacity which is characteristic of the plant body. It has often been stated that any plant cell which has not been structurally modified in its differentiation beyond the possibility of further change ought to be able, given the right conditions, to give rise to an entire plant. The retention of totipotency by differentiated cells has recently been strikingly demonstrated in tissue culture experiments (Steward et al., 31, 32). Many plants, as has been pointed out, can be subdivided into portions which are capable of establishing new individuals. However, in many terrestrial situations the effectiveness of vegetative spread depends more on extent of horizontal development of shoots and roots and degree of specialization of these organs than it does on whether or not natural subdivision of plants takes place.

When a propagule is detached from the parent plant and establishes a new entity, clearly a new organism has resulted even though it may be genetically identical to its parent. On the other hand, if a plant spreads by means of runners, rhizomes, or roots, forming new growth centres which for some time remain attached to the parent and only gradually become separated, a new problem must be faced. In a particular stand of a species, large numbers of apparent individuals may in fact be organically connected, yet these may not be distinguishable from true individuals where connections with the parent have been severed. The problem of identifying the individual is nowhere better illustrated than in an infestation of leafy spurge. For the quantitative ecologist the problem of recognizing the individual becomes acute,

particularly if the connections are subterranean; and his usual procedure is to record numbers of shoots regardless of their individuality.
Thus the basis of quantitative analysis of plant communities is somewhat different from that which underlies the analysis of terrestrial
animal populations in which each entity is a physiologically distinct
organism.

The genetic homogeneity of a population which arises by vegetative multiplication, while it may exactly fit the requirements of the
horticulturist, must necessarily have an adverse effect upon the course
of evolution. The widespread occurrence of this mode of reproduction
must, therefore, reflect distinct advantages which it confers in relatively
unchanging environmental conditions. One rather obvious advantage is
to be found in the supply of nutrients available to the propagule. Even
relatively large seeds contain a limited reserve of nutrients, and vegetative propagules are ordinarily larger and better supplied (Salisbury,
27). This feature is especially prominent in cases in which the new
growth centre develops in attachment to the parent plant and presumably has access to an unlimited supply of nutrients and perhaps
even of water. This continued dependence of a new potential individual upon an already established plant is probably of great significance in explaining the success of rhizomatous and root-bud species
in invading areas of dense and established vegetation in which seedlings are unable to survive competition. It is probable, too, that
bypassing the uncertainties of sexual reproductive methods by means
of vegetative multiplication will confer an advantage upon plants in
certain circumstances. This is obvious in the case of vascular cryptogams which have a separate gametophytic phase. The significance of
this aspect in seed plants is suggested by the widespread occurrence
of agamospermy in which seed dispersal mechanisms are retained
but the embryo is produced asexually.

In the analysis of vegetative propagation, there are certain distinc-
tions which must be kept in mind, but which are sometimes over-
looked or are difficult to make. One of these is the distinction between
true propagation (that is, the potential formation of new individuals)
and simple perennation. If a perennial plant forms buds on a taproot
which merely replace the dead crown of the previous season, this is
not fundamentally a process of propagation. The difficulty is that
such bud production may not be fundamentally different from that
which leads to the formation of new individuals because it occurs
on laterally spreading roots. Korsmo (17) has recognized this distinction by designating perennial herbaceous weeds as "stationary" or

"root-wandering." But many species, such as leafy spurge, are both. The problem is further complicated by the occurrence of degrees of spreading, ranging from barely perceptible lateral extension to advances of several feet in one growing season. A second problem which must be recognized is the distinction between multiplication which occurs in a naturally undisturbed state and that which results only from a more or less severe injury or disturbance. In the case of specialized propagating devices, such as runners or rhizomes, it is relatively easy to conclude that the phenomenon does not depend upon injury. Root buds, however, pose a more difficult problem. Since there is no specialized structure involved, it is necessary to evaluate the importance of injury or disturbance very carefully. Thus, Wittrock (34) has distinguished between what he calls "additional" buds, those which arise spontaneously on uninjured roots, and "reparative" buds, those which develop only when the root is injured or removed from the parent plant. In varying circumstances, both can provide effective vegetative multiplication. Furthermore, it is evident that many species which produce root shoots without injury respond to injury by an increased shoot production. In leafy spurge the production of root buds occurs as a regular phenomenon on apparently undisturbed plants; but the expansion of these buds into aerial shoots, and even the initiation of buds, is greatly enhanced by injury. In the cases cited here, the disturbance was considerable; but presumably less drastic injury can lead to similar, but less dramatic responses.

A final point to be noted concerns the work which has been done on vegetative propagation rather than the phenomenon itself. The literature on this subject is voluminous and workers with a variety of interests have had occasion to investigate the phenomenon. Unfortunately, where this literature has dealt with propagation by underground organs, there is often a notable lack of precision in describing the participating structures. Rhizomes and roots are frequently confused and, most frustratingly, a wide variety of terms are employed which do not indicate the morphological nature of the organ. While such precise information may not be necessary for measurements of rate of spread, it is indispensable for any morphogenetic or physiological analysis. Consequently many of the older studies of vegetative multiplication require a re-investigation before they can serve as a basis for experimental work, even at the practical level of weed control.

This paper has attempted to show that vegetative multiplication is an important factor to be considered in attempting to understand the composition of a flora and the changes or evolution which it undergoes. The specific examples considered here have, hopefully, served to illustrate this point. The fact is, however, that at this stage we cannot state precisely how important a factor it is in the evolution of the flora of Canada. A survey based upon Breitung's (5) *Annotated Catalogue of the Vascular Flora of Saskatchewan,* for example, indicates that approximately 35 per cent of the perennial species (30 per cent of the vascular flora) propagate vegetatively in some way. This figure alone is enough to cause interest; but an assessment of the proportion of the total number of individual plants that is comprised of species that are multiplying vegetatively would be of more significance. The widely distributed and numerically abundant aspen is extremely dependent upon vegetative reproduction and in the prairie region seems to rely upon it exclusively. One of the most abundant conifer species of the boreal forest, black spruce, reproduces vegetatively, at least under some conditions. The flora of the prairie region in recent years has been intruded upon by a number of introduced species which persist and spread in large part by vegetative means. These examples suggest that it is unlikely that the number of species alone is a real indication of the importance of this phenomenon.

There have been some generalizations which suggest that vegetative propagation may have special significance in northern floras, including that of Canada. It has been noted (Gustafsson, 15) that there is an increase in the occurrence of vegetatively propagating species at progressively higher latitudes in the northern hemisphere, along with a comparable increase in agamospermy, and that arctic floras contain a high proportion of such species. The advantages of non-sexual reproduction under extreme climatic conditions have already been outlined. It has also been shown (Gustafsson, 15; Stebbins, 30) that the occurrence of polyploidy is high among such species; but there is no general agreement that the relationship between polyploidy and vegetative reproduction is a causal one. Löve and Löve (19) argue that the same conditions in the north favour the emergence of both characteristics independently. On the other hand, the inability of species numbers alone to measure the significance of vegetative propagation in the flora has already been recognized. It is tempting, however, to speculate that, just as the evolution of herbaceous angiosperms from woody ancestors apparently occurred in relation to climatic refrigeration beginning in Tertiary time and was accentuated by glaciation (Sinnott and Bailey, 29), so the evolution of vegetative propagation as a significant reproductive mechanism in angiosperms may have had a similar history. It may not be assumed, however, that vegetative multiplication in itself is a recent plant invention. If current reconstructions of Silurian and Devonian land plants are accurate (Andrews, 1), the earliest terrestrial vegetation of which we have any real knowledge was characterized by the widespread occurrence of vegetative increase. This observation might lend some credence to the view that the plants which inhabited the swamps of Rhynie and the Gaspé region 375 million years ago may have been living under rather unfavourable conditions (Arnold, 2). It may be significant that, in spite of excellent preservation in the Rhynie beds, the gametophytic or sexual generation of these plants has not been found (although recent work by Pant (22) has cast some doubt upon the absence of gametophytes). It is possible that these ancient plants persisted and spread with little or no reliance upon sexual reproduction, much as does modern *Lycopodium*.

The only general conclusion that can be drawn from this brief review is that the phenomenon of vegetative multiplication is badly in need of intensive study. A survey of the floras of several major regions of the world, representing different ecological conditions, to determine the frequency of occurrence of vegetative propagation, not only in terms of numbers of species but of the abundance of each species as well, might provide a real basis for the evaluation of the significance of this mode of reproduction. It is important that such a survey include an evaluation of the degree to which each species depends upon vegetative multiplication. Moreover, it is essential that in each case the kind of reproductive mechanism involved be understood. From the point of view of ecological significance, it may well be that the grouping of various vegetative reproductive mechanisms obscures real differences between them. In a particular environment, for example, rhizomes and bud-producing roots might have very different influences upon the composition of a plant community. At the same time, it will be most important to conduct intensive morphological, anatomical, developmental, and physiological studies on selected species having various types of vegetative multiplication in order to provide a sound basis for the interpretation of the results of generalized surveys.

ACKNOWLEDGMENT

Extra-mural Research Grant no. 70 from the Canada Department of Agriculture has supported the research of the present authors referred to in this paper.

REFERENCES

1. ANDREWS, H. N. 1961. Studies in Paleobotany. John Wiley & Sons, Inc., New York. 487 pp.

2. ARNOLD, C. A. 1947. An Introduction to Paleobotany. McGraw-Hill Book Co. Inc., New York. 433 pp.

3. BAKKE, A. L. 1936. Leafy spurge: Euphorbia esula L. Iowa State Coll. Agric. Expt. Sta., Res. Bull. No. 198, 207–246.

4. BEST, K. F. 1963. Note on the extent of lateral spread of field bindweed. Can. J. Pl. Sci. 43: 230–232.

5. BREITUNG, A. J. 1957. Annotated catalogue of the vascular flora of Saskatchewan. Am. Midl. Nat. 58: 1–72.

6. CHARLTON, W. A. 1962. The underground system of Linaria vulgaris Hill. M.Sc. Thesis, Univ. of Saskatchewan.

7. COOPER, W. S. 1911. Reproduction by layering in the black spruce. Botan. Gaz. 55: 452–457.

8. COUPLAND, R. T. 1961. A reconsideration of grassland classification in the northern great plains of North America. J. Ecol. 49: 135–167.

9. COUPLAND, R. T. and J. F. ALEX. 1954. Distribution of the underground parts of leafy spurge (Euphorbia esula L.). Can. J. Agr. Sci. 34: 161–76.

10. COUPLAND, R. T. and J. F. ALEX. 1955. Distribution of vegetative buds on the underground parts of leafy spurge (Euphorbia esula L.). Can. J. Agr. Sci. 35: 76–82.

11. COUPLAND, R. T., G. W. SELLECK, and J. F. ALEX. 1955. The reproductive capacity of vegetative buds on the underground parts of leafy spurge (Euphorbia esula L.). Can. J. Agr. Sci. 35: 477–484.

12. COUPLAND, R. T., S. ZILKE, and G. W. SELLECK. 1963. Spread of toadflax in Saskatchewan. Can. J. Pl. Sci. 43: 214–221.

13. FRAZIER, J. C. 1943. Nature and rate of development of root system of Convolvulus arvensis. Botan. Gaz. 104: 417–425.

14. FULLER, G. D. 1913. Reproduction by layering in the black spruce. Botan. Gaz. 55: 452–457.

15. GUSTAFSSON, A. 1948. Polyploidy, life-form and vegetative reproduction. Hereditas 34: 1–22.

16. HORTON, K. W., and J. C. LEES. 1961. Black spruce in the foothills of Alberta. Forest Res. Br., Tech. Note No. 110: 1–54.

17. KORSMO, E. 1930. Unkräuter im Ackerbau der Neuzeit. Berlin. 580 pp.

18. LEBLANC, J. H. 1955. A mode of vegetative propagation in black spruce. Pulp and Paper Mag. Can. 56(6): 76–82.

19. LÖVE, A., and DORIS LÖVE. 1949. The geobotanical significance of polyploidy: I, Polyploidy and latitude. Portugaliae Acta Biol. A. 273–352.

20. LYON, FLORENCE M. 1901. A study of the sporangia and gametophytes of Selaginella apus and Selaginella rupestris. Botan. Gaz. 32: 124–141, 170–194.

21. MAINI, J. S. 1960. Invasion of grassland by Populus tremuloides in the northern great plains. Ph.D. thesis, Univ. of Saskatchewan.

22. PANT, D. D. 1962. The gametophyte of the Psilophytales (in Proc. of the Summer School of Botany at Darjeeling, P. Maheshwari, B. M. Johri and I. K. Vasil, eds.). Ministry Sci. Res. and Cult. Affairs, New Delhi. 276–301.

23. PLACE, I. C. M. 1950. Origin of reproduction on black spruce swamps. Can. Dept. Resources and Dept. Forestry, Forest Res. Br., Div. Silv. Leaf. No. 38.

24. RAJU, M. V. S., T. A. STEEVES, and R. T. COUPLAND. 1963. Developmental studies on Euphorbia esula L.: Morphology of the root system. Can. J. Botany 41: 579–589.

25. Raju, M. V. S., T. A. Steeves, and R. T. Coupland. 1964. On the regeneration of root fragments of leafy spurge (*Euphorbia esula* L.). Weeds Res. 4(1): 1–11.
26. ⸺ 1965. On the occurrence of root buds on perennial plants in Saskatchewan. Can. J. Botany 44: 33–37.
27. Salisbury, E. J. 1942. The Reproductive Capacity of Plants. G. Bell and Sons, Ltd., London. 244 pp.
28. Selleck, G. W., R. T. Coupland, and C. Frankton. 1962. Leafy spurge in Saskatchewan. Ecol. Monographs 32: 1–29.
29. Sinnot, E. W., and I. W. Bailey. 1915. The evolution of herbaceous plants and its bearing on certain problems of geology and climatology. J. Geology 23: 289–306.
30. Stebbins, G. L. 1950. Variation and Evolution in plants. Columbia Univ. Press, New York. 643 pp.
31. Steward, F. C., Marion O. Mapes, and Joan Smith. 1958. Growth and organized development of cultured cells: I, Growth and division of freely suspended cells. Am. J. Botany 45: 693–803.
32. Steward, F. C., Marion O. Mapes, and Kathryn Mears. 1958. II. Growth and organized development of cultured cells. Organization in cultures grown from freely suspended cells. Am. J. Botany 45: 705–708.
33. Vincent, A. B. 1964. Comparative growth of black spruce seedlings and layers under an alder canopy. Woodlands Rev. Sec., Pulp and Paper Mag., Can. Forest Res. Br., Contr. No. 630: 1–3.
34. Wittrock, V. B. 1884. Om rotskott hos örtartade växter, med särskild hänsyn till deras olika biologiska betydelse. Botan. Notiser 21–37.